PAUL WELLER

for guitar tab

wise publications

london / new york / paris / sydney / copenhagen / madrid

exclusive distributors:

music sales limited
8/9 frith street, london w1v 5tz, england

music sales pty limited
120 rothschild avenue, rosebery, nsw 2018, australia

order no. am935847
isbn 0-7119-5582-4
this book © copyright 1996 by wise publications

book design by michael bell design
compiled by peter evans
edited by arthur dick
music processed by seton music graphics
guitar kindly loaned by rose morris
front cover: tim o'sullivan/fsp, all other photographs courtesy of
retna and rex features

your guarantee of quality:
as publishers, we strive to produce every book to the
highest commercial standards

the music has been freshly engraved and the book has
been carefully designed to minimise awkward page turns and
to make playing from it a real pleasure

particular care has been given to specifying acid-free, neutral-sized
paper made from pulps which have not been elemental chlorine bleached

this pulp is from farmed sustainable forests and was produced with
special regard for the environment

throughout, the printing and binding have been planned to ensure a
sturdy, attractive publication which should give years of enjoyment

if your copy fails to meet our high standards, please inform us
and we will gladly replace it

music sales' complete catalogue describes thousands of titles and
is available in full colour sections by subject, direct from music sales limited
please state your areas of interest and send a cheque/postal order
for £1.50 for postage to: music sales limited,
newmarket road, bury st. edmunds, suffolk ip33 3yb

visit the internet music shop at
http://www.musicsales.co.uk

printed in the united kingdom by
redwood books limited, trowbridge, wiltshire.

bull-rush 6

foot of the mountain 17

has my fire really gone out? 24

into tomorrow 34

out of the sinking 42

stanley road 52

sunflower 62

the changingman 90

time passes... 70

wild wood 76

woodcutter's son 84

tablature & instructions explained 4

tablature & instructions explained

The tablature stave comprises six lines, each representing a string on the guitar as illustrated.

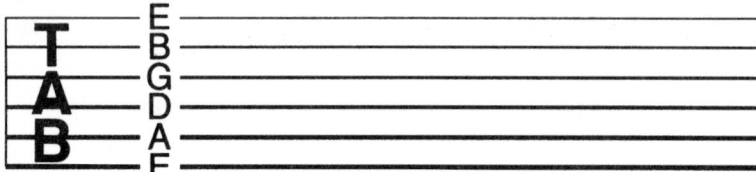

A number on any of the lines indicates, therefore, the string and fret on which a note should be played.

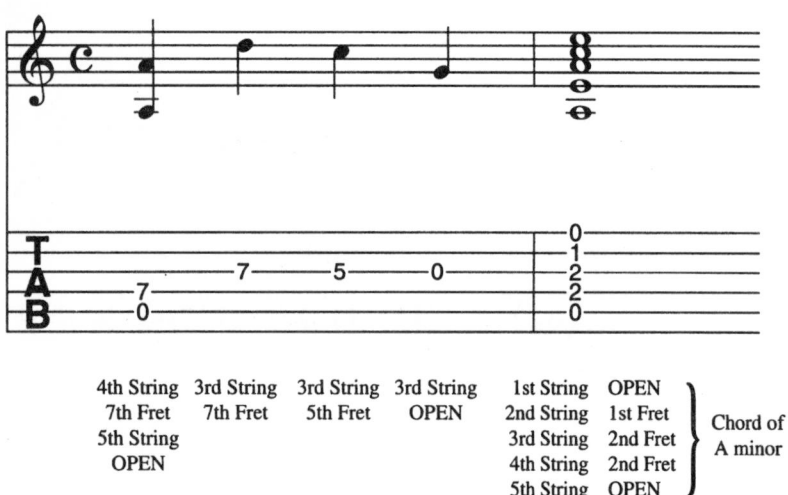

4th String 7th Fret 5th String OPEN	3rd String 7th Fret	3rd String 5th Fret	3rd String OPEN	1st String OPEN 2nd String 1st Fret 3rd String 2nd Fret 4th String 2nd Fret 5th String OPEN	Chord of A minor

A useful hint to help you read tablature is to cut out small squares of self-adhesive paper and stick them on the upper edge of the guitar neck adjacent to each of the frets, numbering them accordingly. Be careful to use paper that will not damage the finish on your guitar.

Finger Vibrato

Tremolo Arm Vibrato

Glissando

Strike the note, then slide the finger up or down the fretboard as indicated.

Tremolo Strumming

This sign indicates fast up and down stroke strumming.

8va

This sign indicates that the notes are to be played an octave higher than written.

loco

This instruction cancels the above.

This note-head indicates the string is to be totally muted to produce a percussive effect.

P.M. = Palm mute

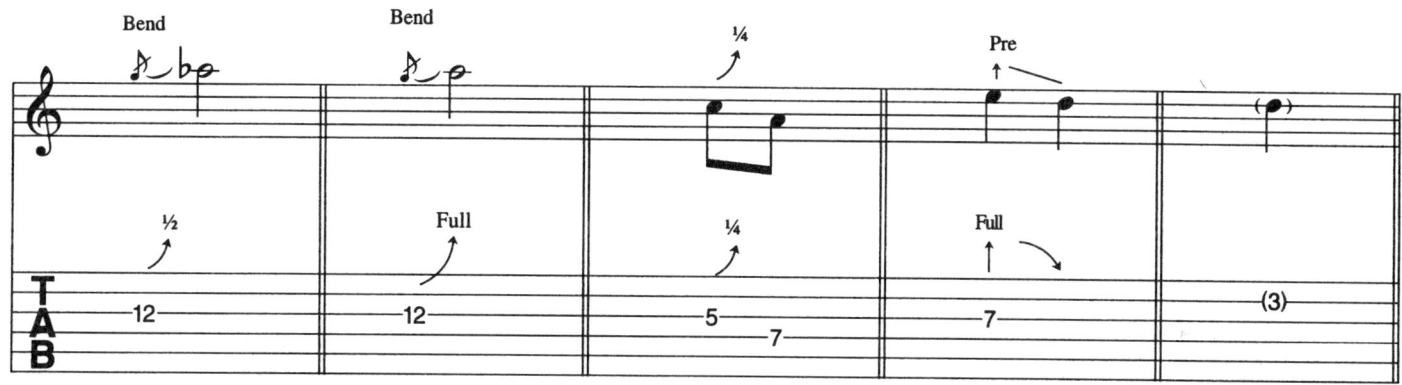

HALF TONE BEND

Play the note G then bend
the string so that the pitch rises
by a half tone (semi-tone).

FULL TONE BEND

DECORATIVE BEND

PRE-BEND

Bend the string as indicated,
strike the string and release.

GHOST NOTE

The note is half sounded

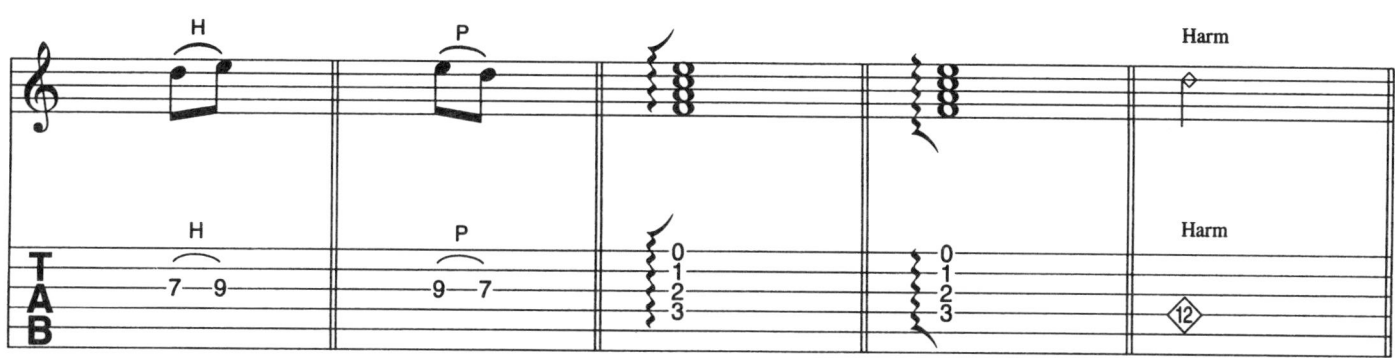

BEND & RELEASE

Strike the string, bend it as
indicated, then release the bend
whilst it is still sounding.

BEND & RESTRIKE

Strike the string, bend or gliss
as indicated, then restrike the
string where the symbol occurs.

UNISON BEND

Strike both strings
simultaneously then
immediately bend the
lower string as indicated.

STAGGERED UNISON BEND

Strike the lower string and bend as
indicated; whilst it is still sounding
strike the higher string.

HAMMER-ON

Hammer a finger down
on the next note without
striking the string again.

PULL-OFF

Pull your finger off the string
with a plucking motion to
sound the next note without
striking the string again.

RAKE-UP

Strum the notes upwards
in the manner of an
arpeggio.

RAKE-DOWN

Strum the notes downwards
in the manner of an
arpeggio.

HARMONICS

Strike the string whilst
touching it lightly at the
fret position shown.
Artificial Harmonics, (A.H.),
will be described in context.

bull-rush

words & music by paul weller

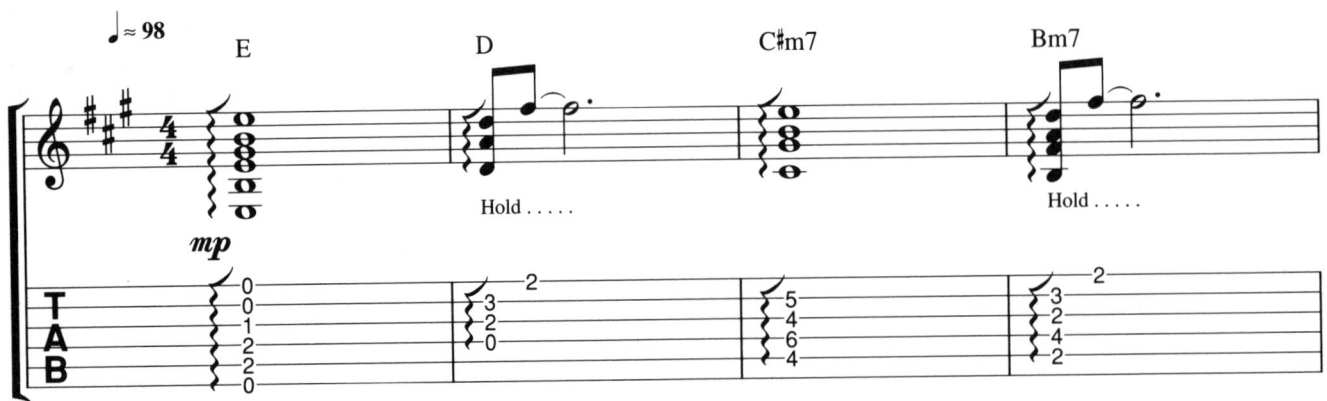

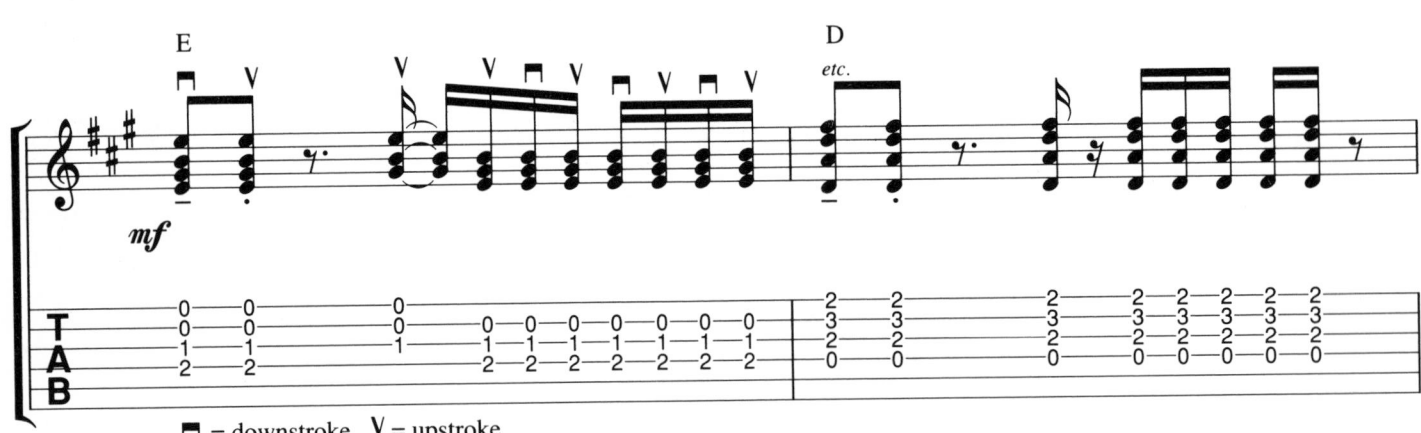

◻ = downstroke   V = upstroke

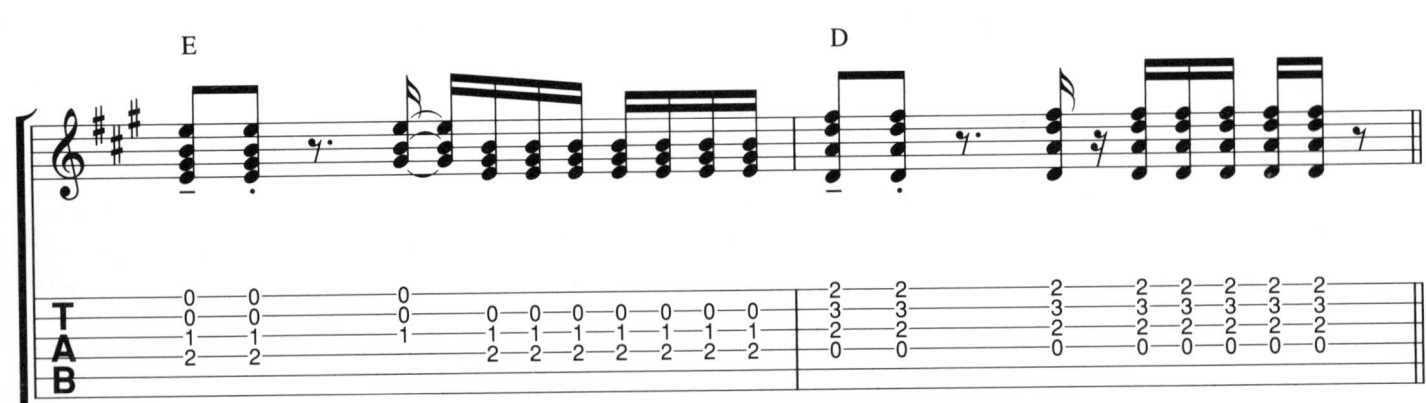

Verse:

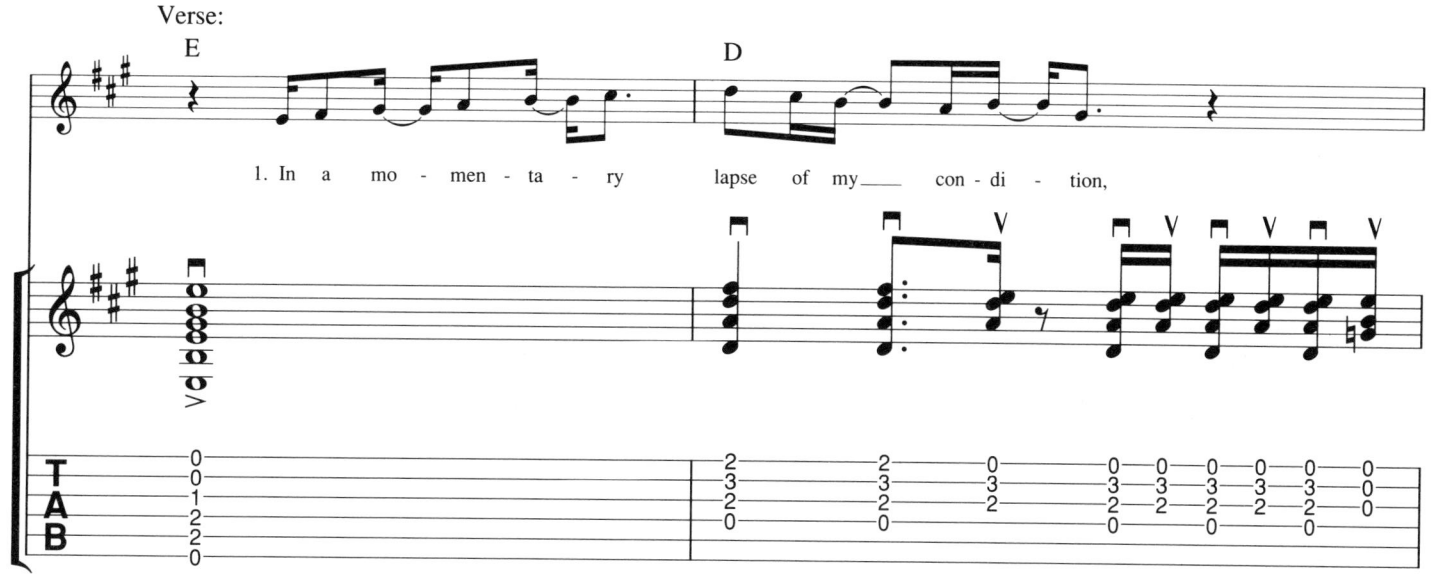

1. In a mo - men - ta – ry lapse of my___ con - di – tion,

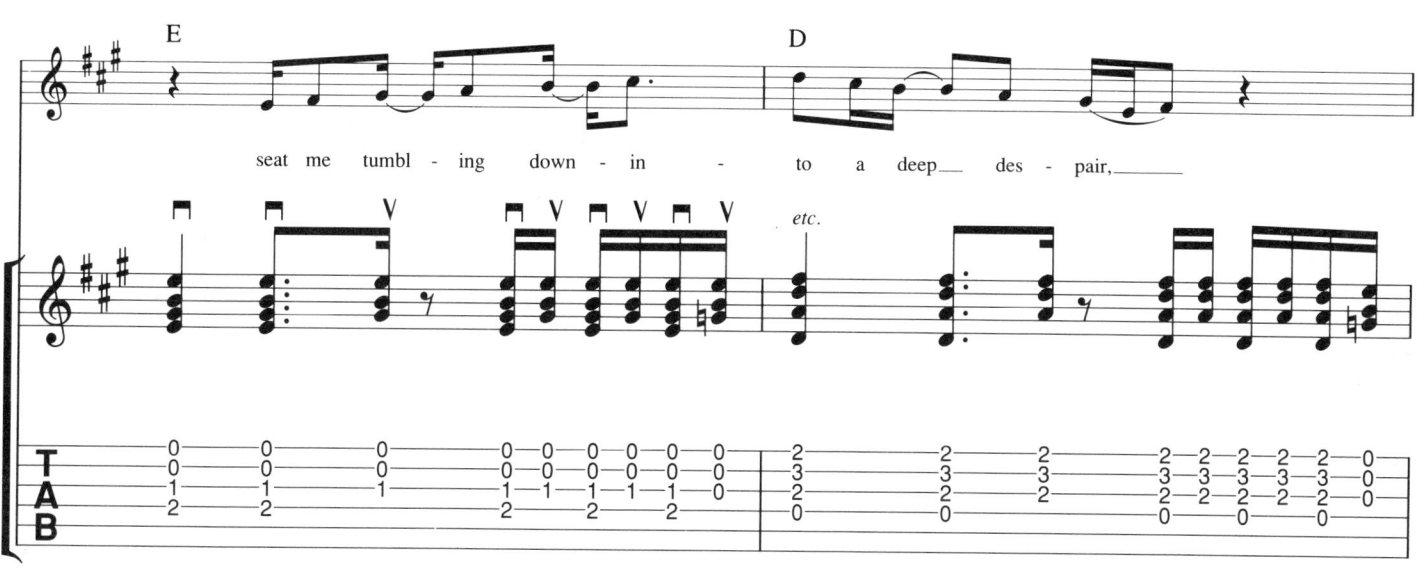

seat me tumbl – ing down in – to a deep___ des – pair,___

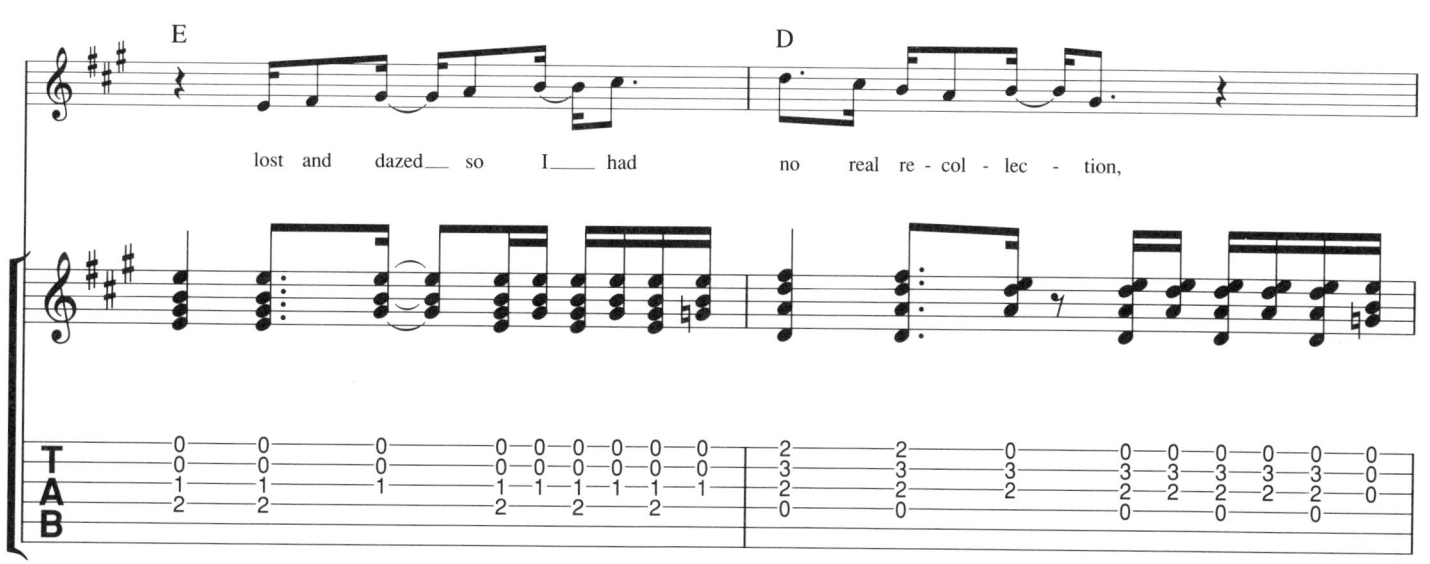

lost and dazed___ so I___ had no real re - col - lec – tion,

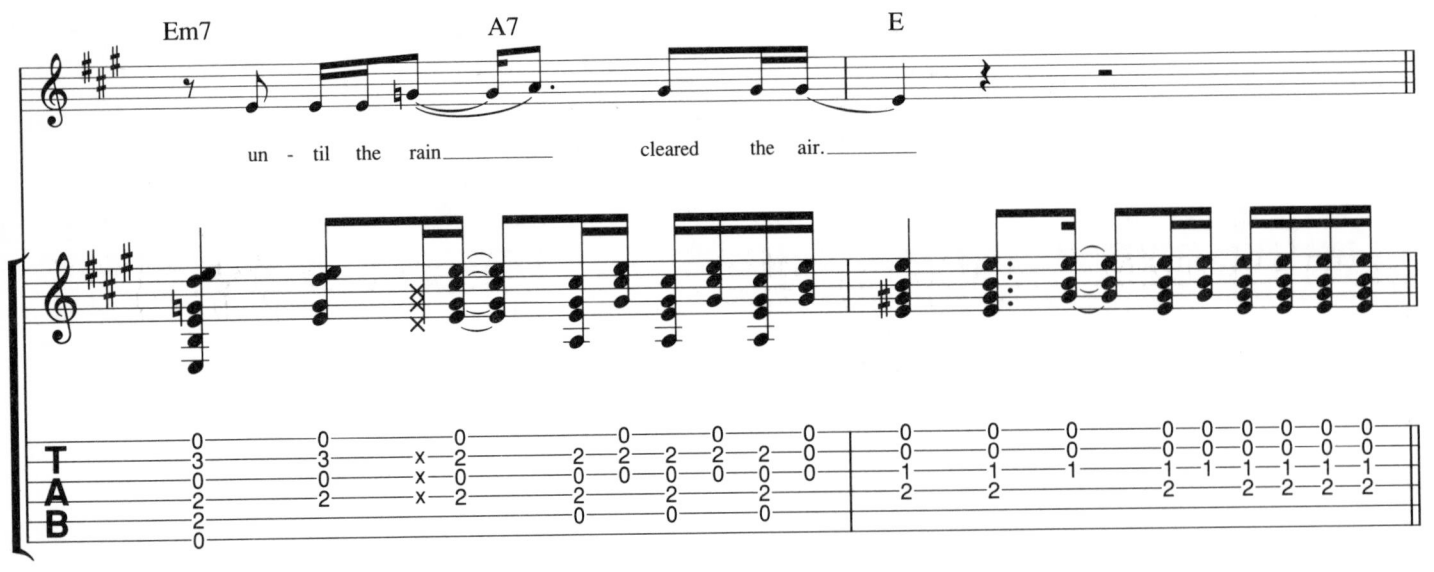

un - til the rain_____ cleared the air._____

Verse:

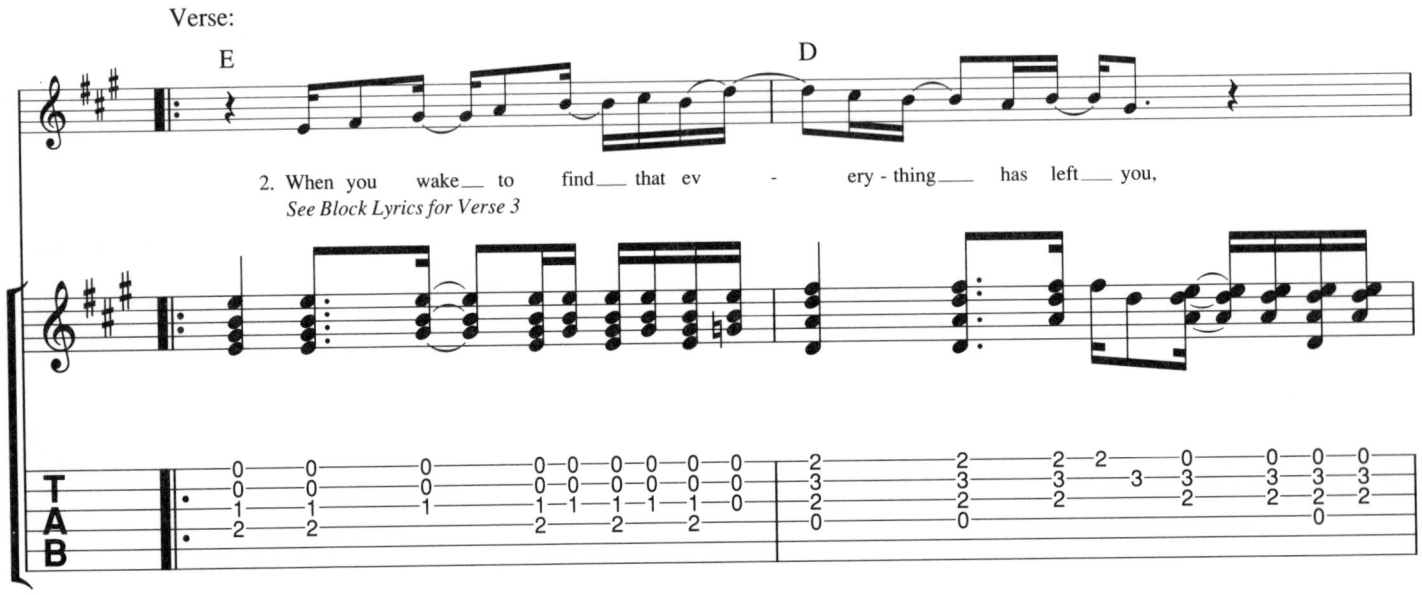

2. When you   wake__ to   find__ that ev - ery-thing___ has left__ you,
See Block Lyrics for Verse 3

and the clothes__ you   wear__ be - long to some - one else,_____

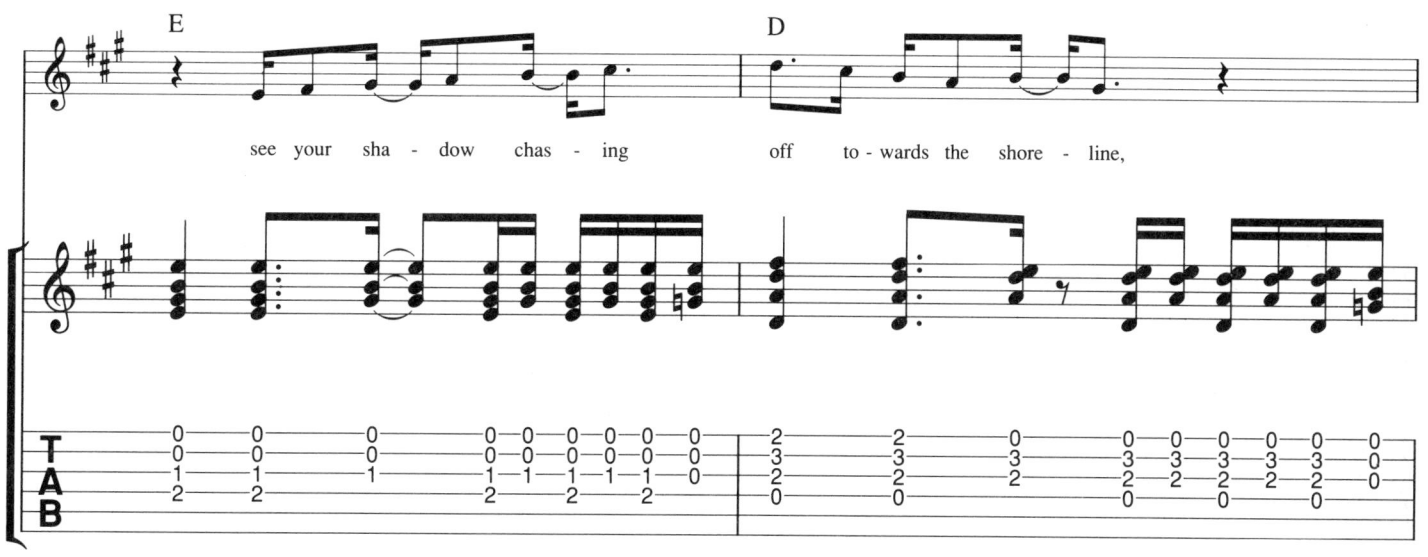

see your sha - dow chas - ing   off to - wards the shore - line,

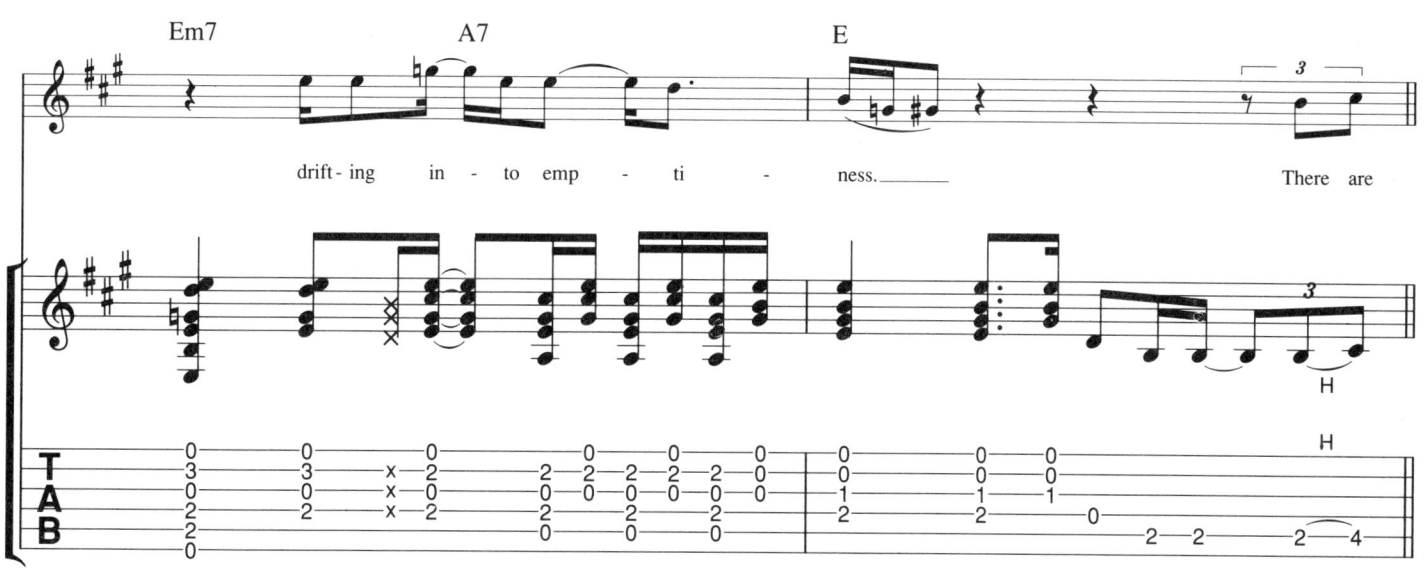

drift - ing in - to emp - ti - ness.___   There are

Chorus:

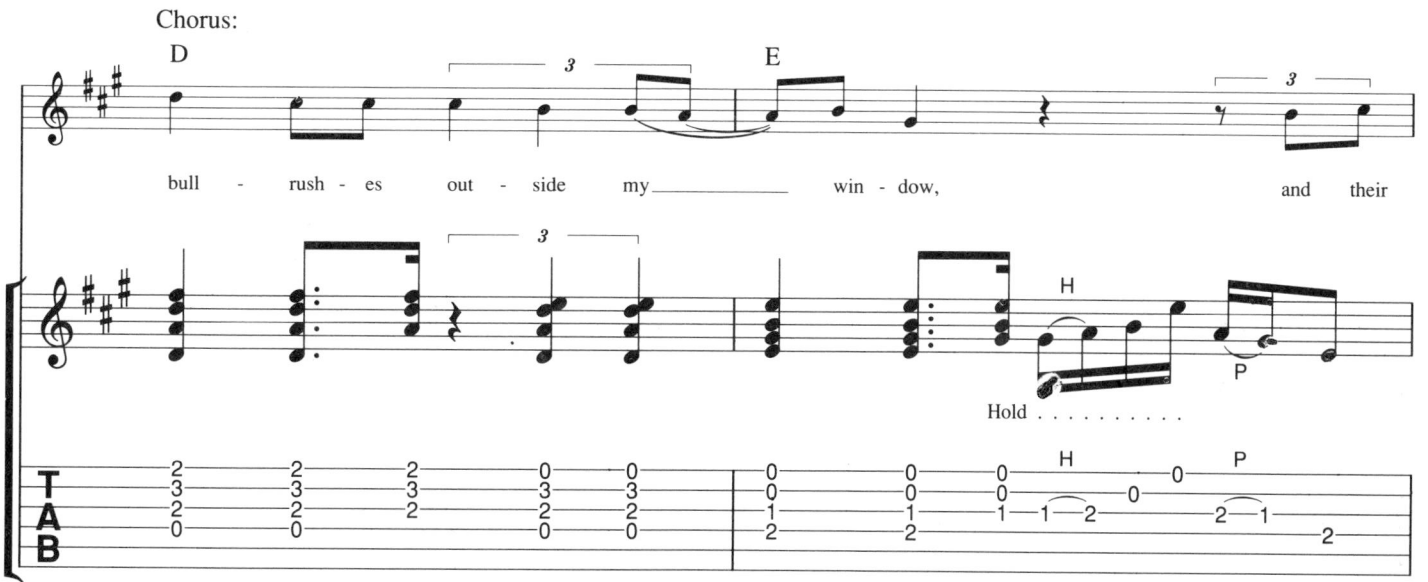

bull - rush - es out - side my___ win - dow,   and their

Hold . . . .

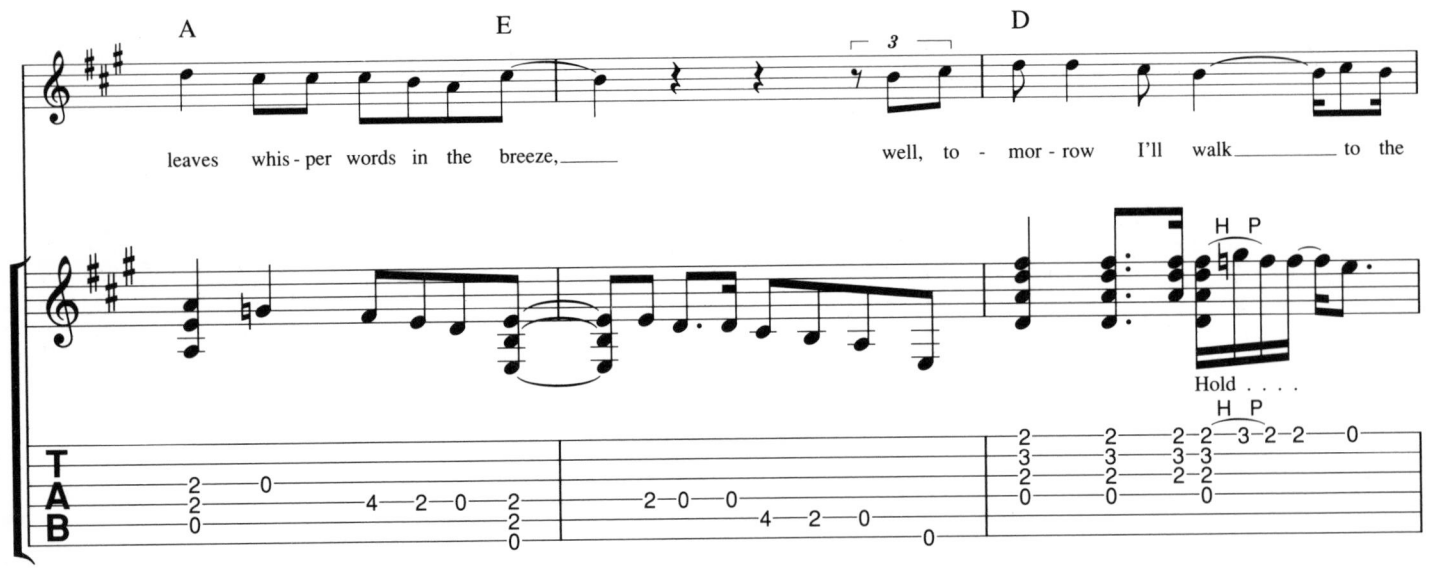

leaves whis-per words in the breeze,___ well, to - mor-row I'll walk___ to the

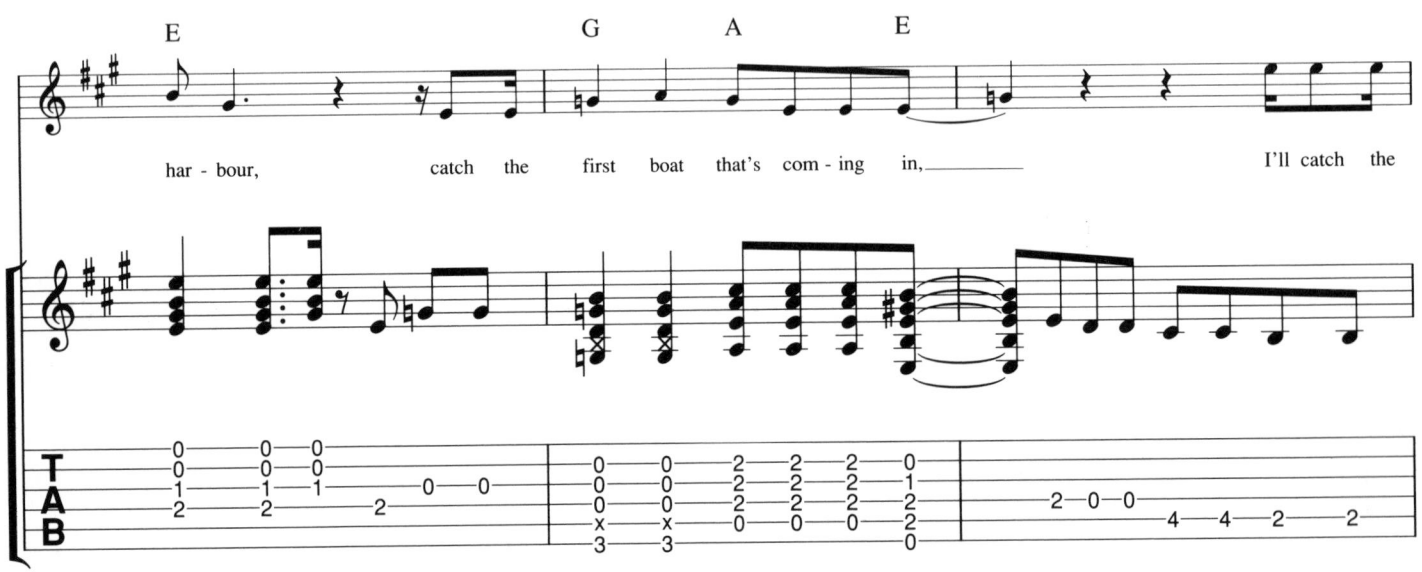

har - bour, catch the first boat that's com - ing in,___ I'll catch the

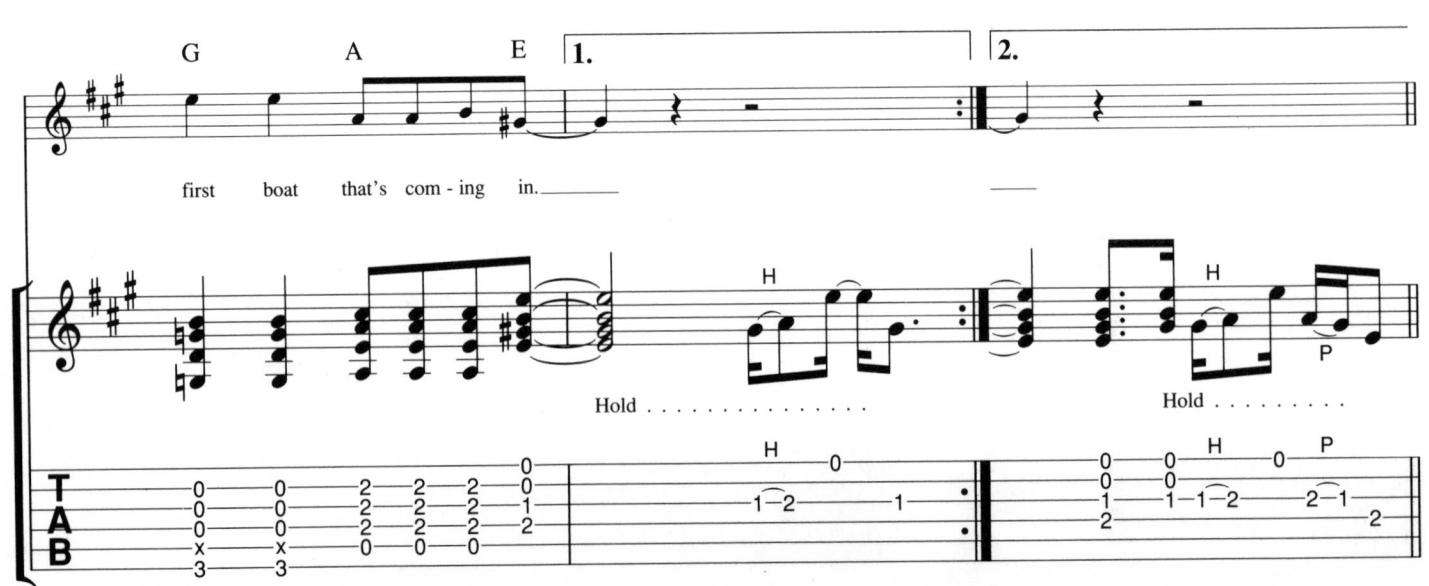

first boat that's com - ing in.___

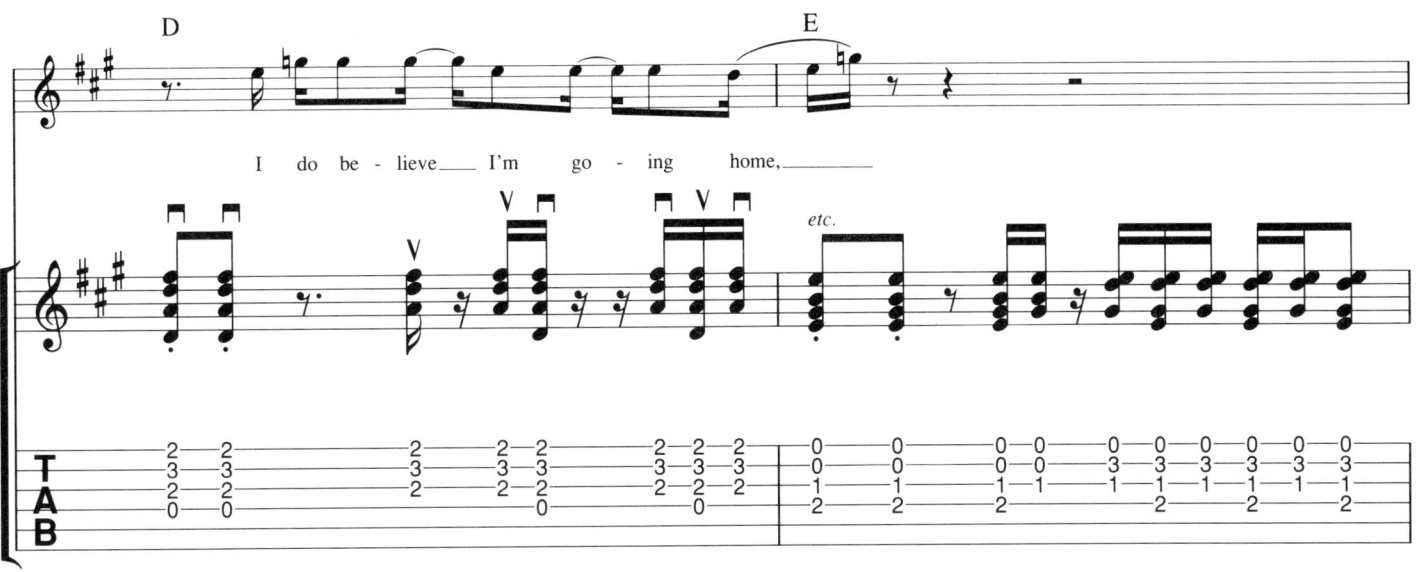

I do be - lieve___ I'm go - ing home,_____

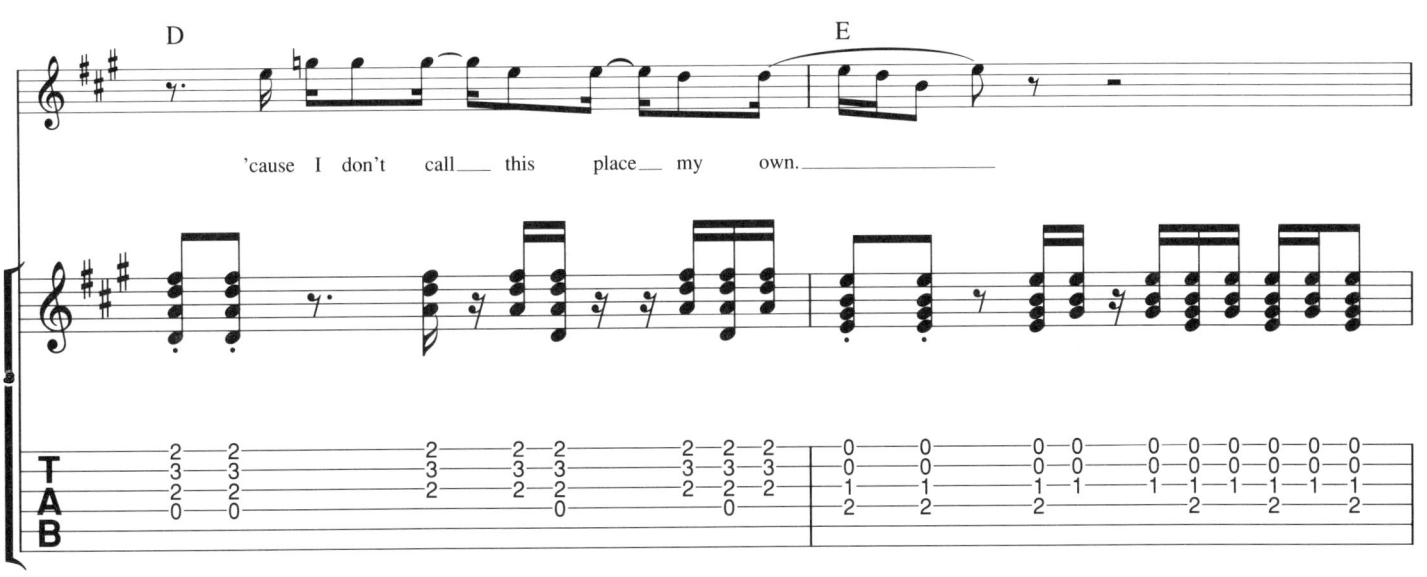

'cause I don't call___ this place___ my own._____

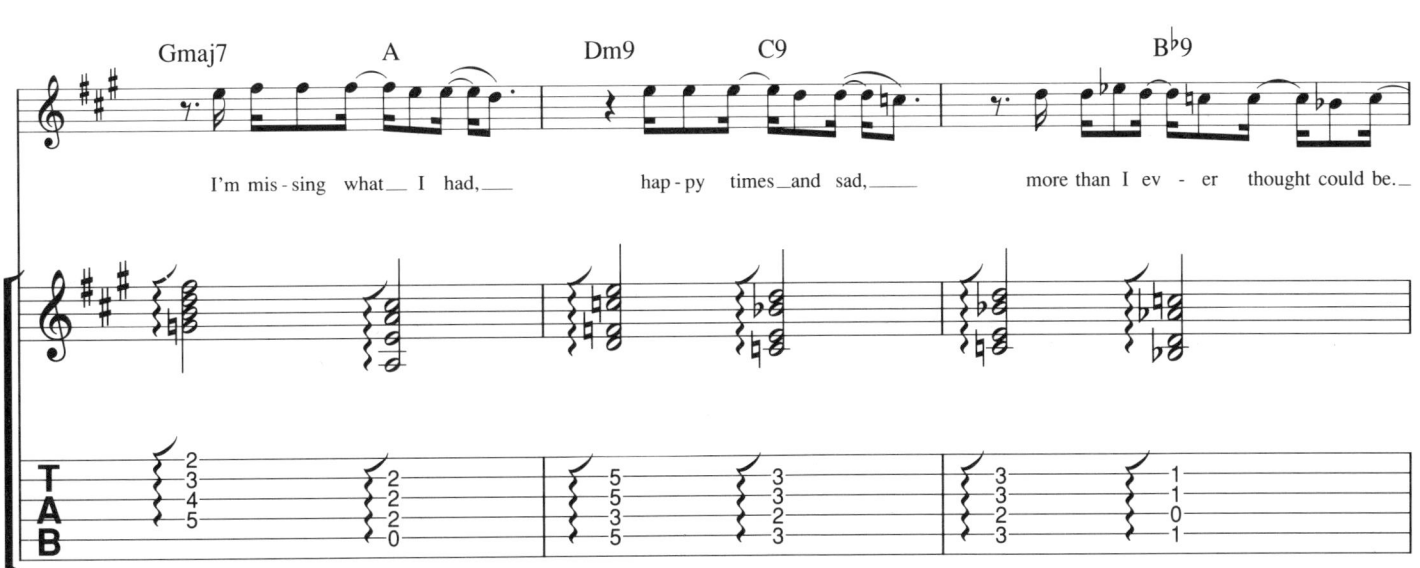

I'm mis - sing what__ I had,___ hap - py times_and sad,___ more than I ev - er thought could be.__

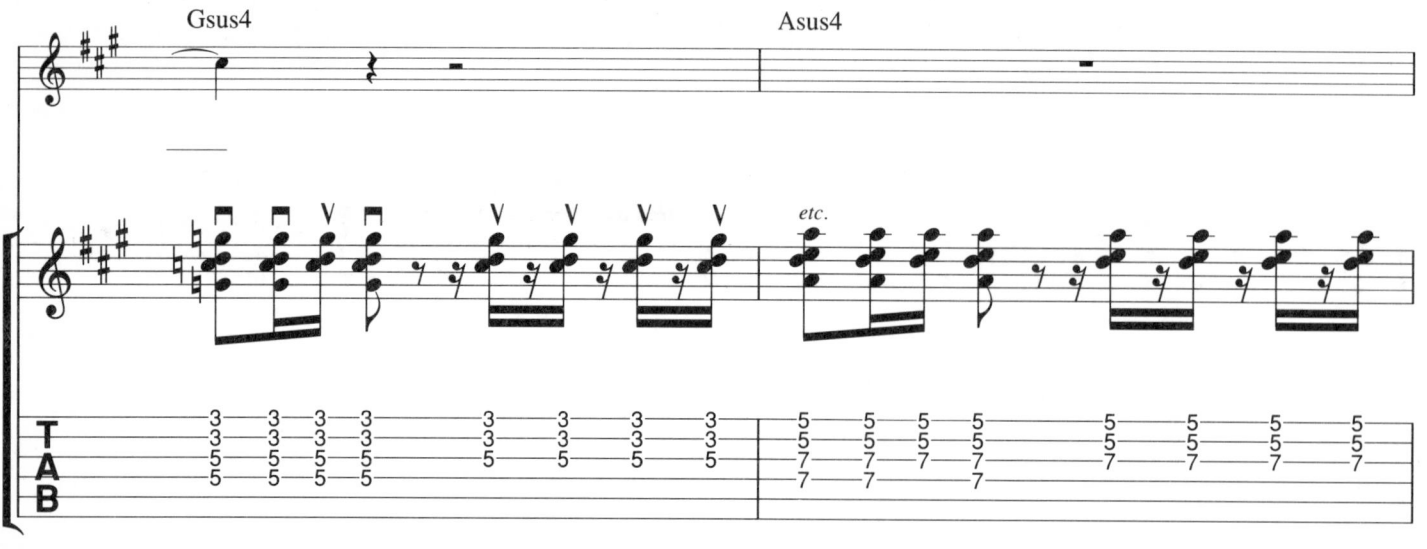

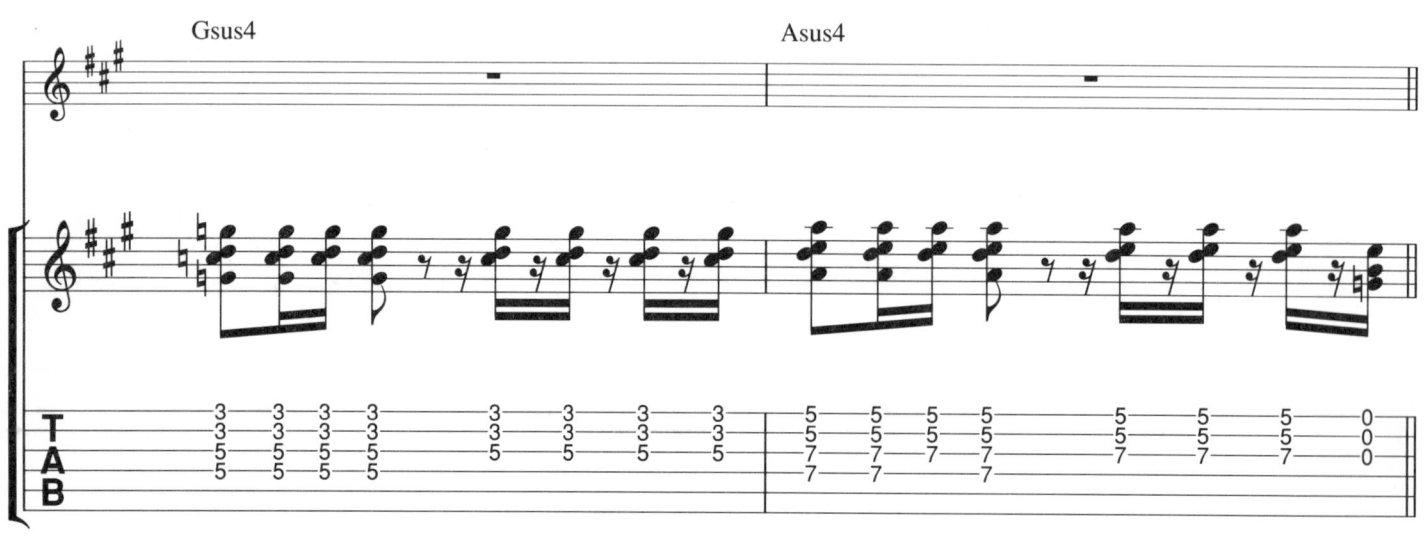

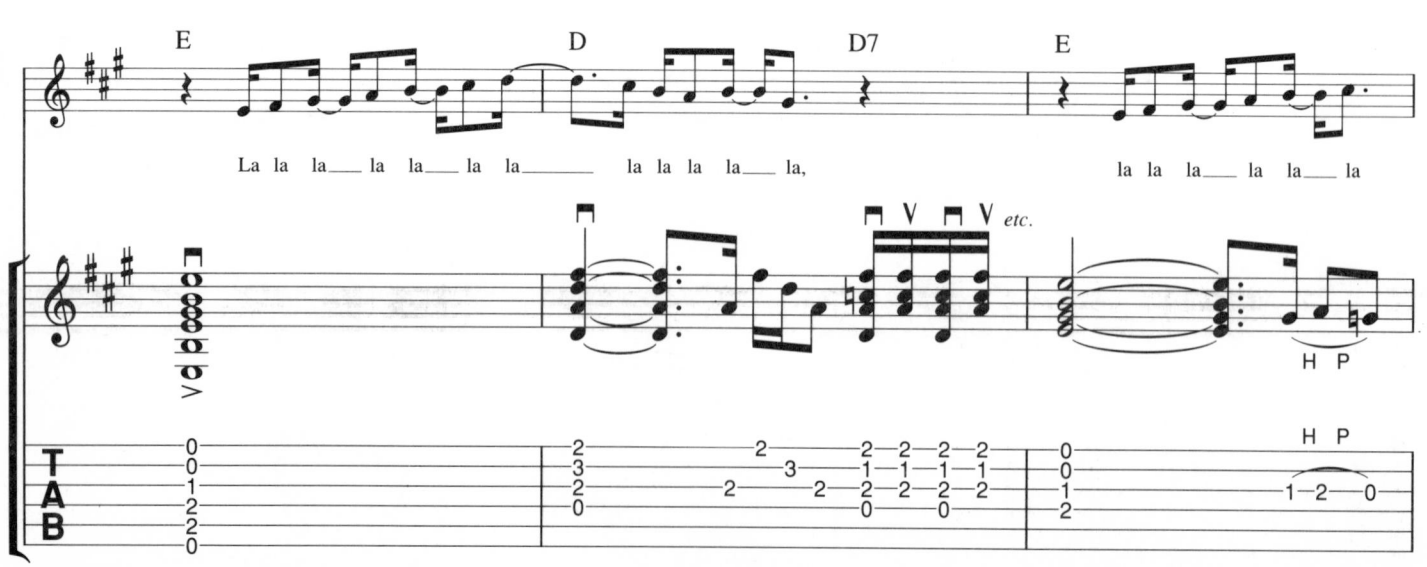

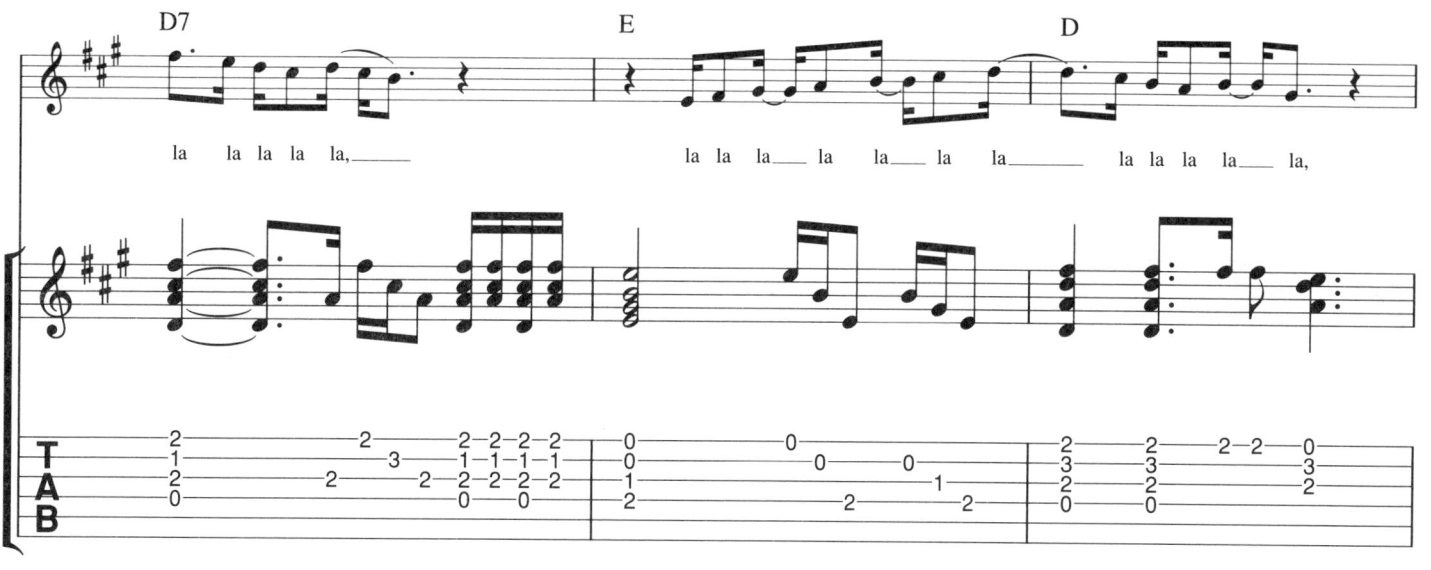

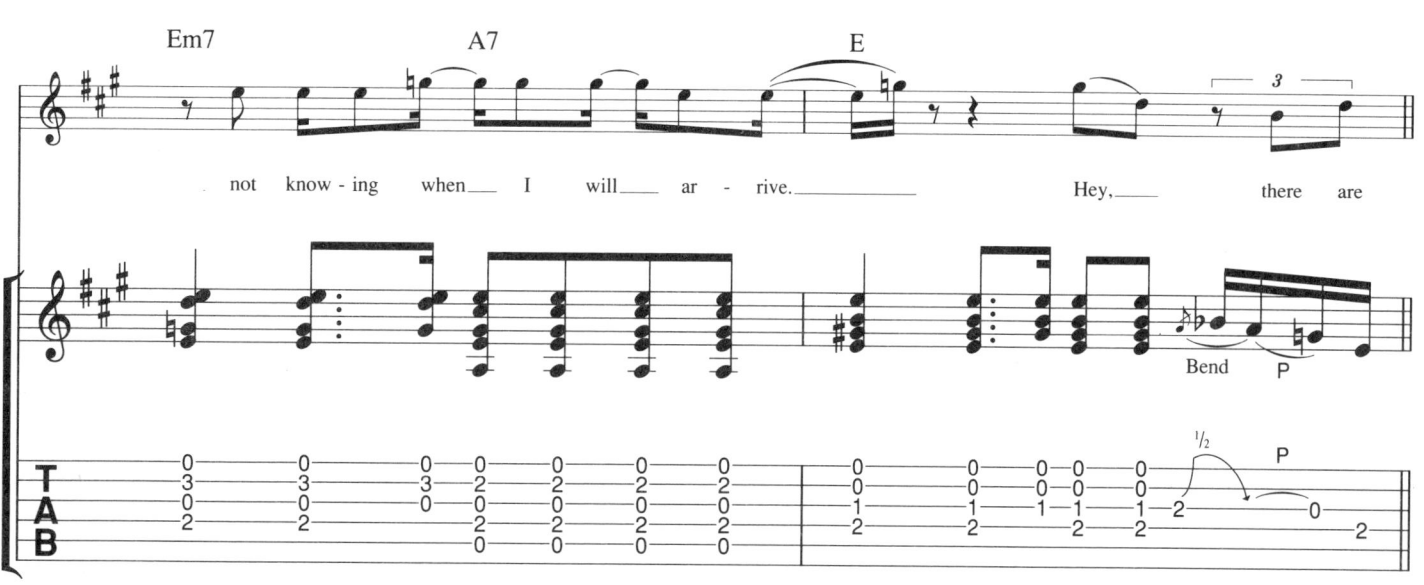

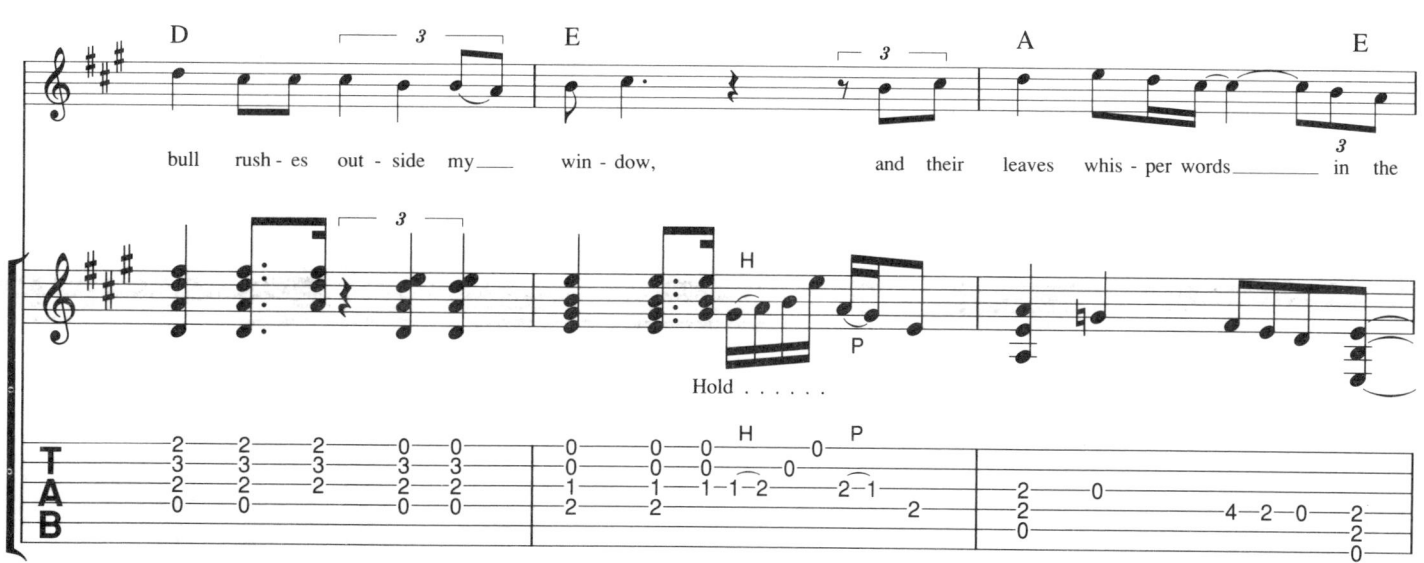

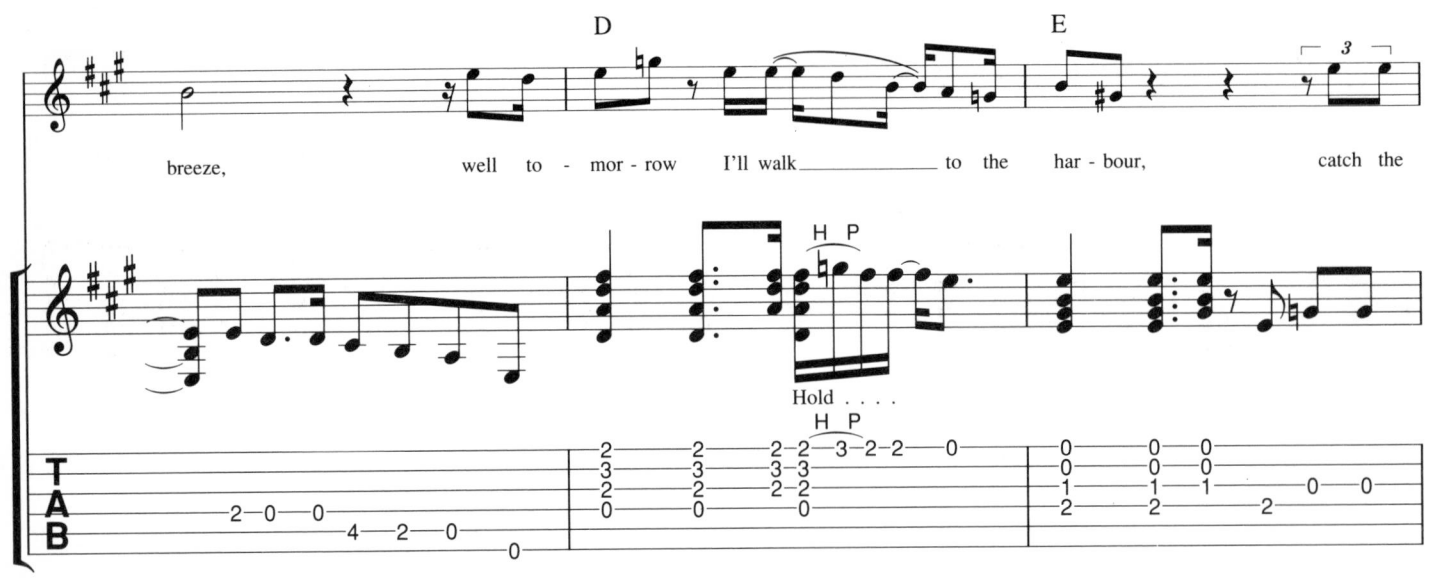

breeze,   well to - mor - row I'll walk_____ to the har - bour,   catch the

first boat that's com - ing in,_____   I'll catch the first boat that's com - ing in._____

_____ Hey, I'll catch the   first boat that's com - ing in,_____   yeah,_____

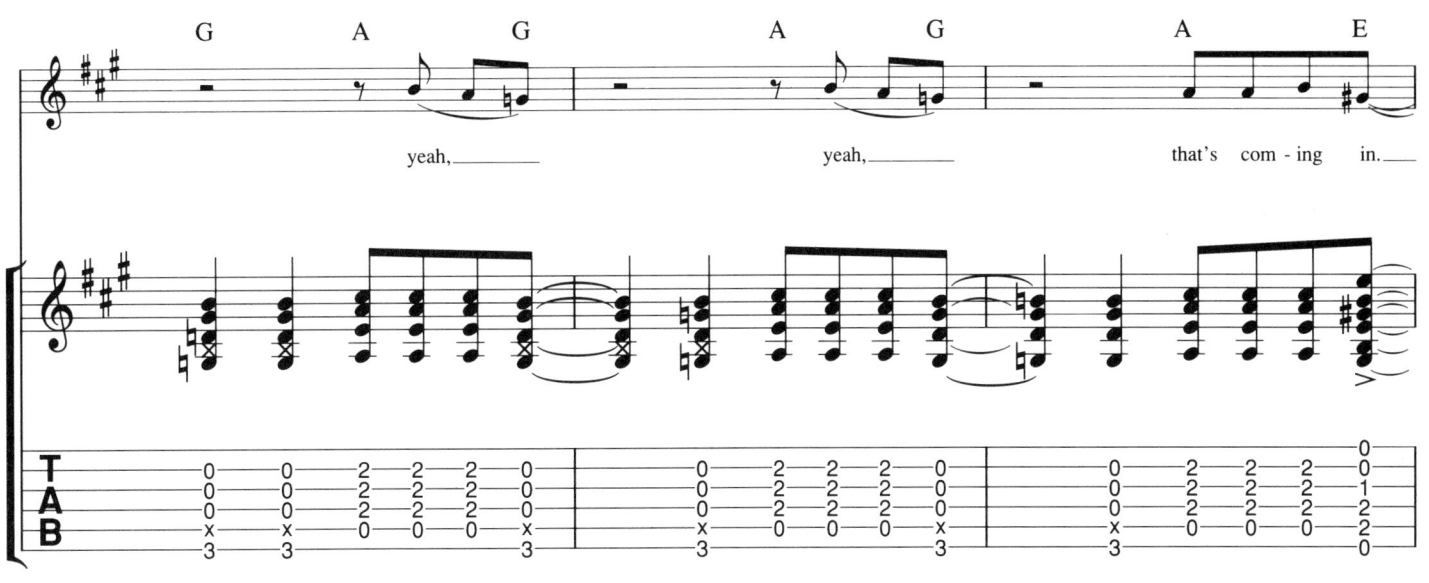

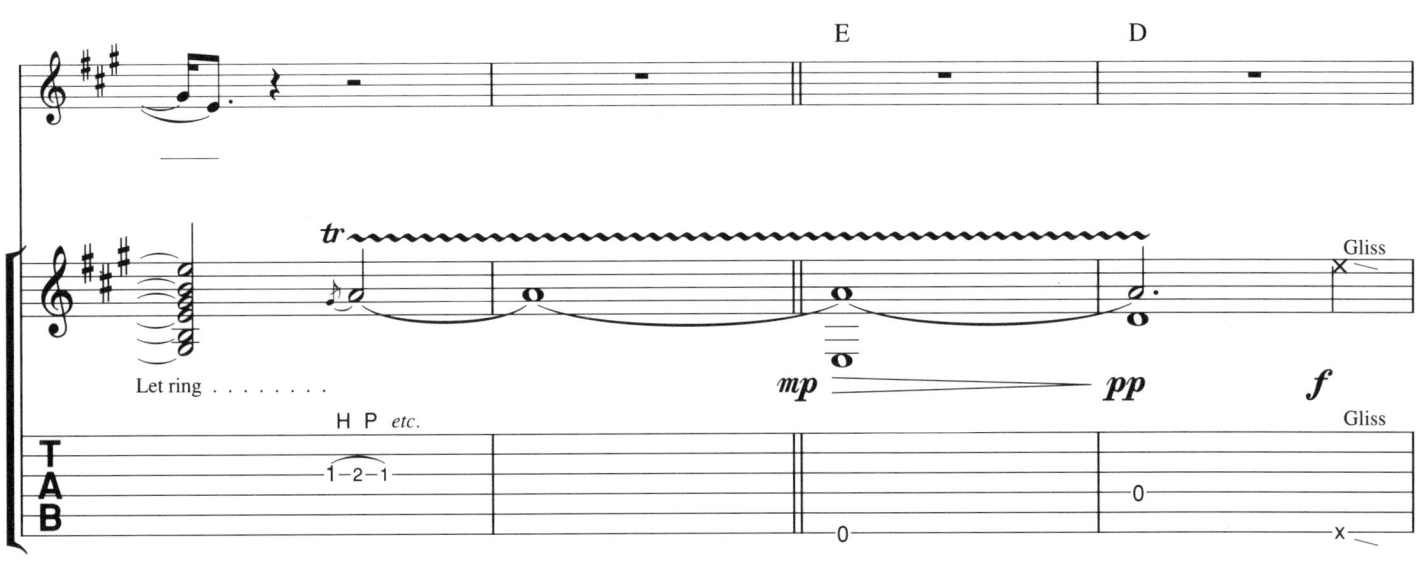

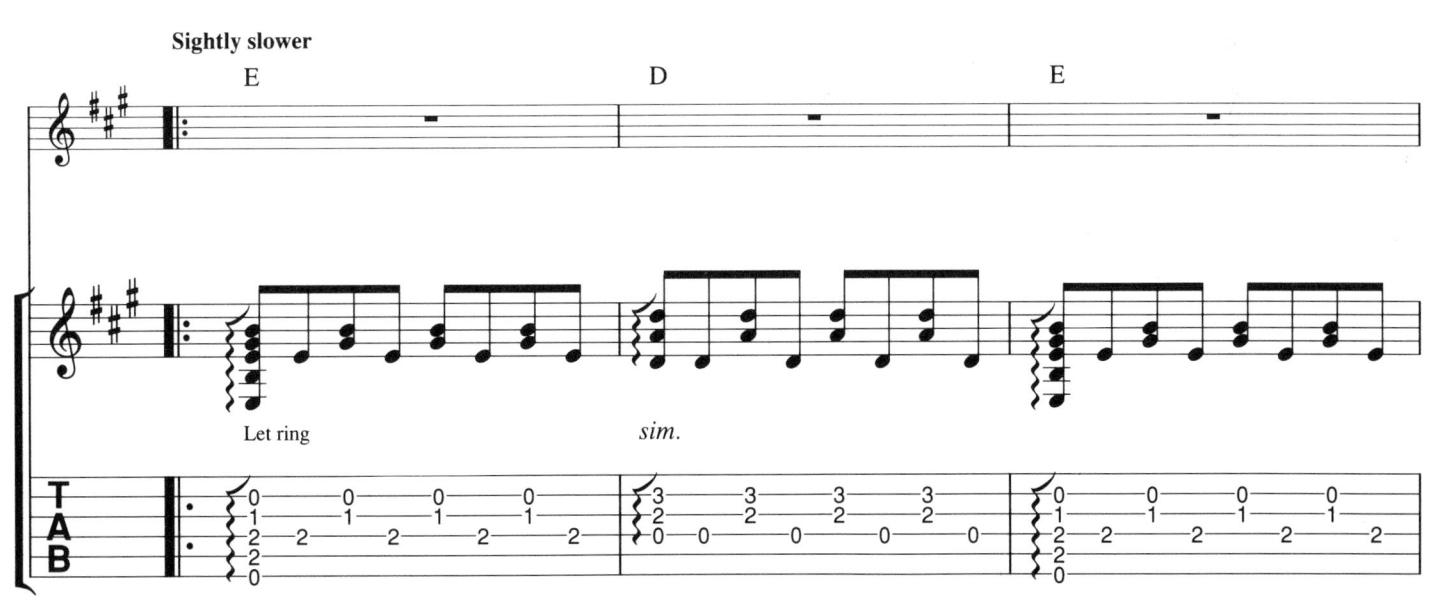

Verse 3:
Like a child too small to reach the front door handle
Maybe just too scared to know what I would find
Now I feel I'm strong enough to take a slow ride
Not knowing when I will arrive.

foot of the mountain

words & music by paul weller

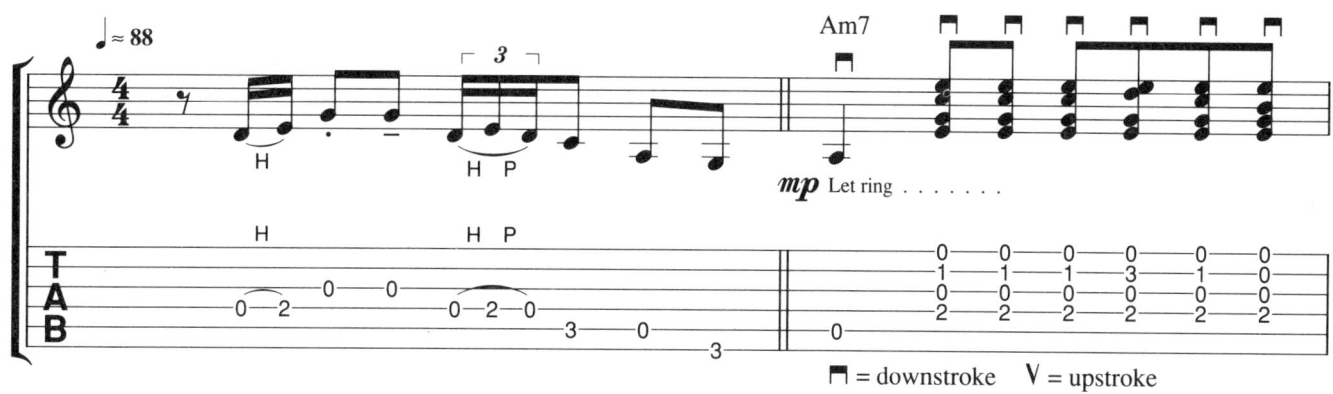

= downstroke   V = upstroke

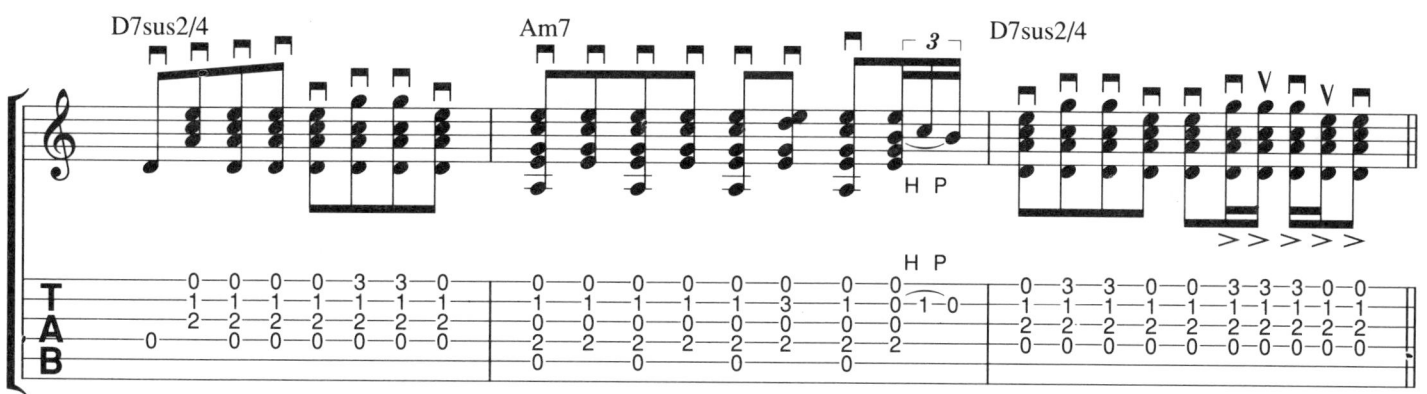

Verse:

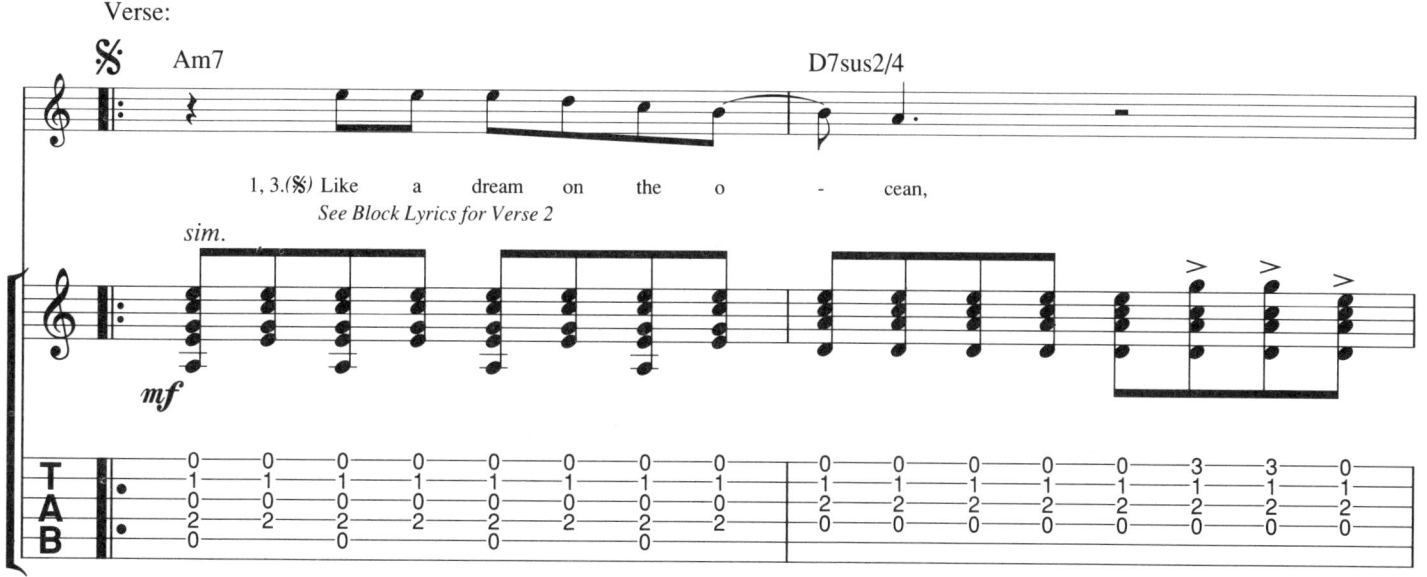

1, 3.(%) Like a dream on the o - cean,

See Block Lyrics for Verse 2

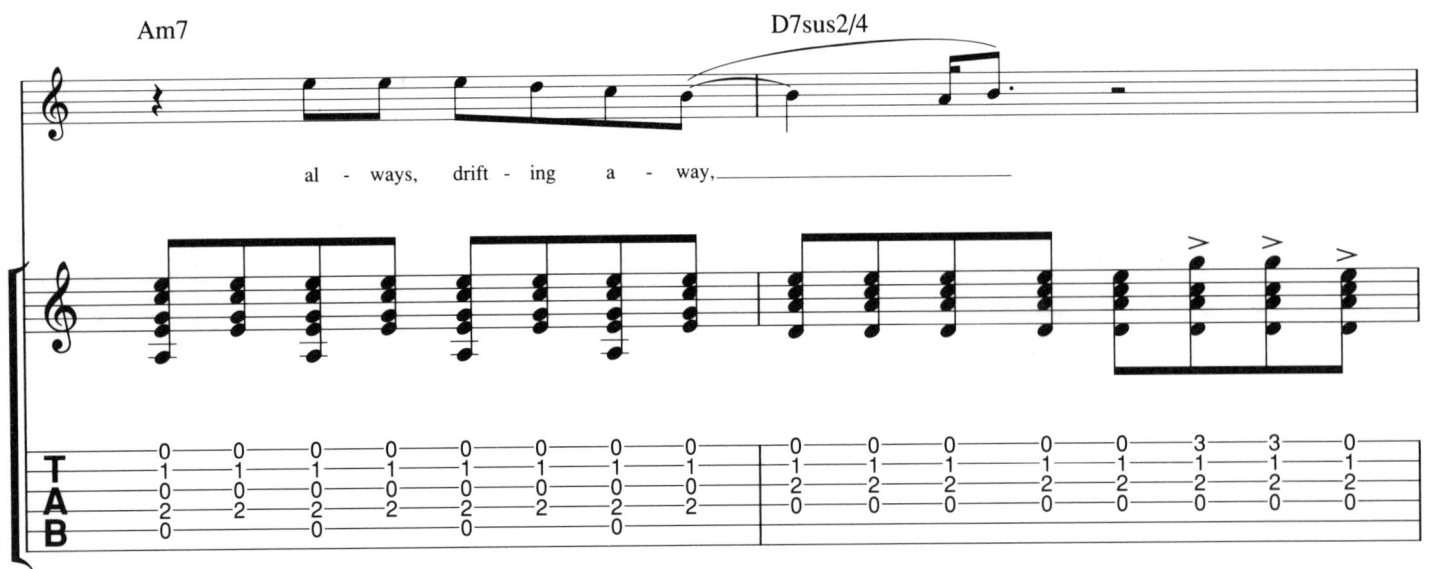

al - ways, drift - ing a - way,_____

To Coda ✛

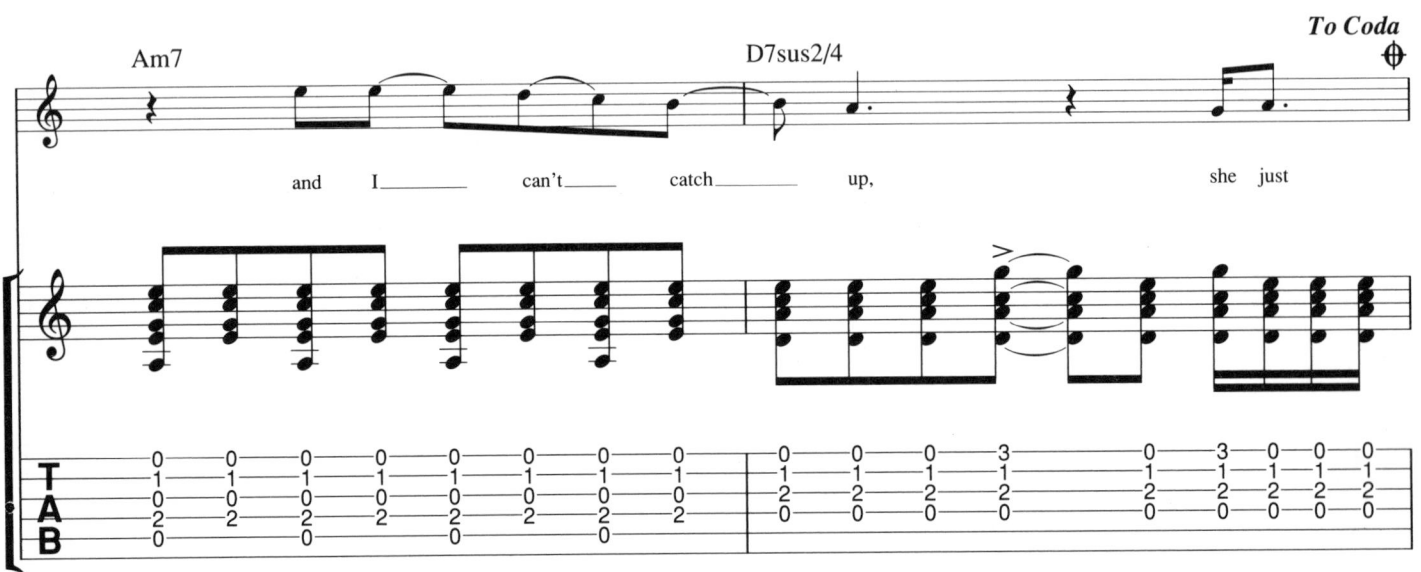

and I____ can't____ catch____ up, she just

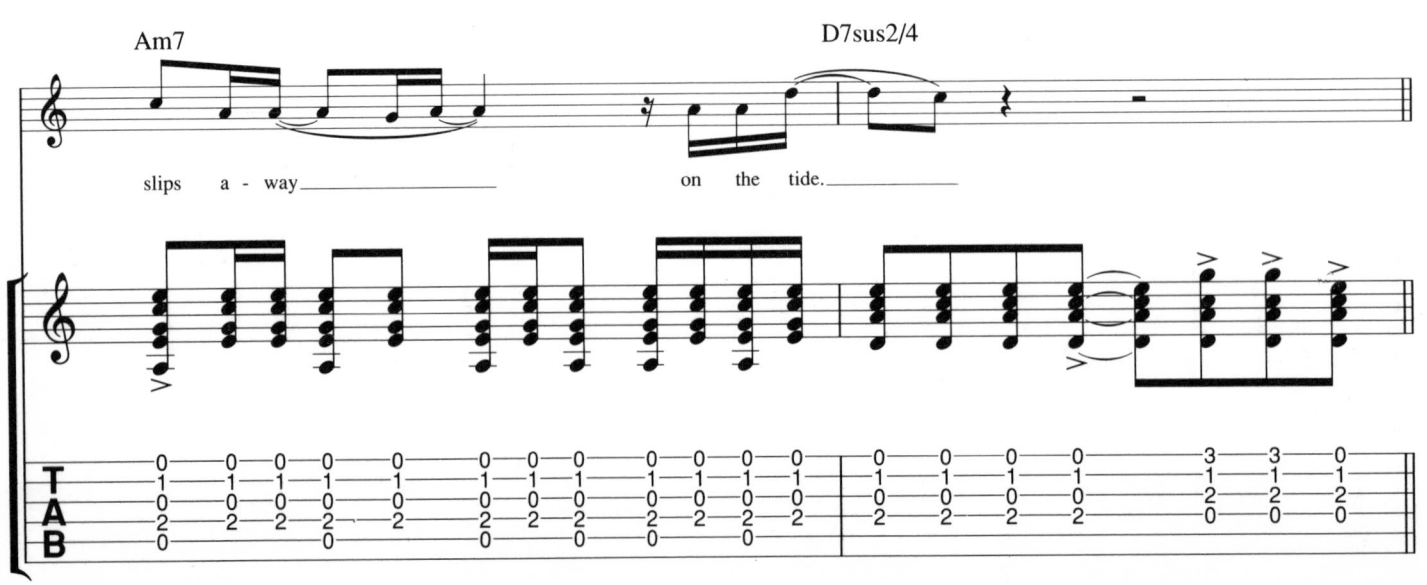

slips a - way_____ on the tide._____

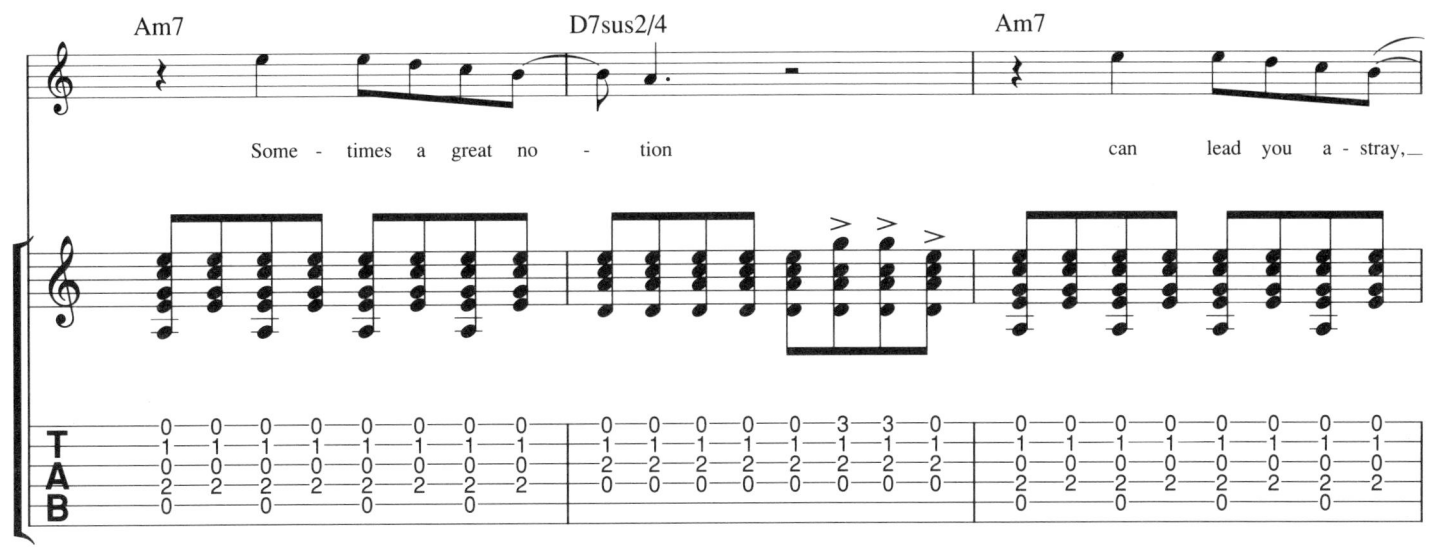

Some - times a great no - tion can lead you a - stray,

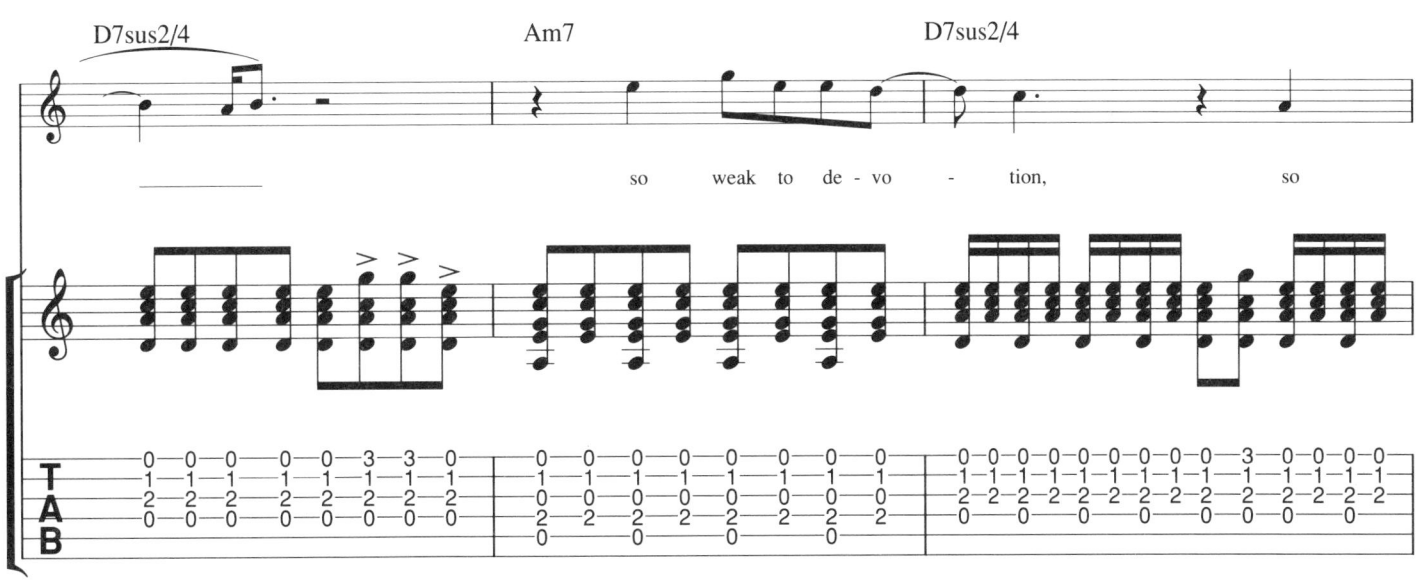

so weak to de - vo - tion, so

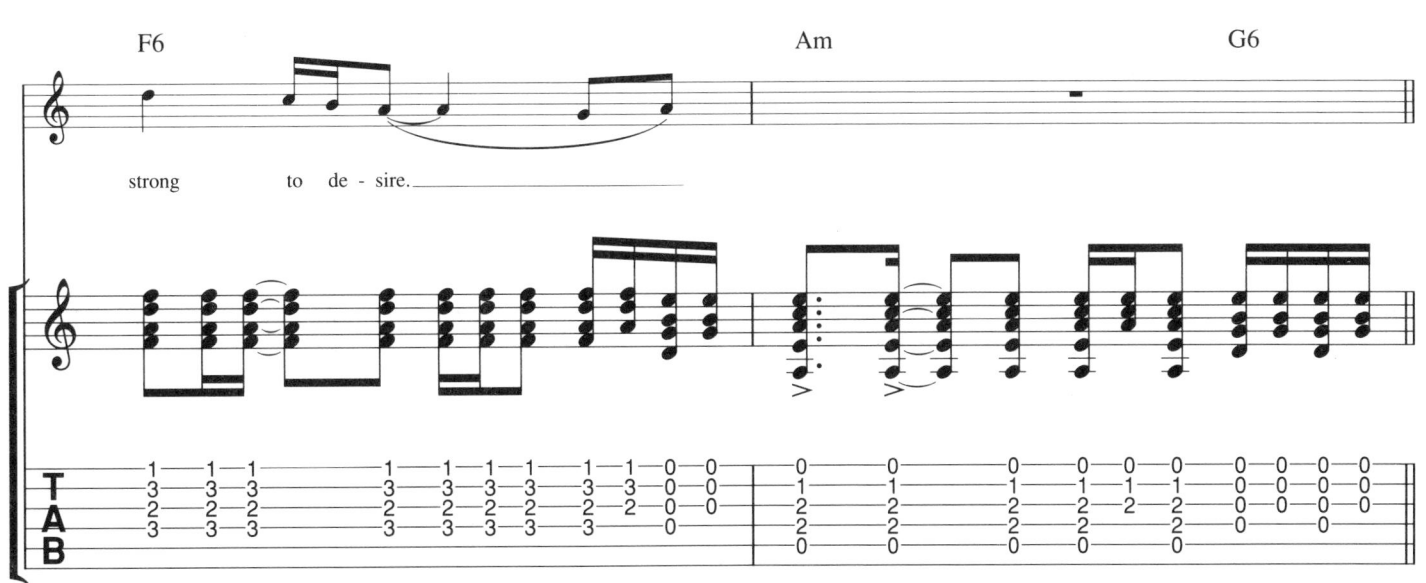

strong to de - sire.

Chorus:

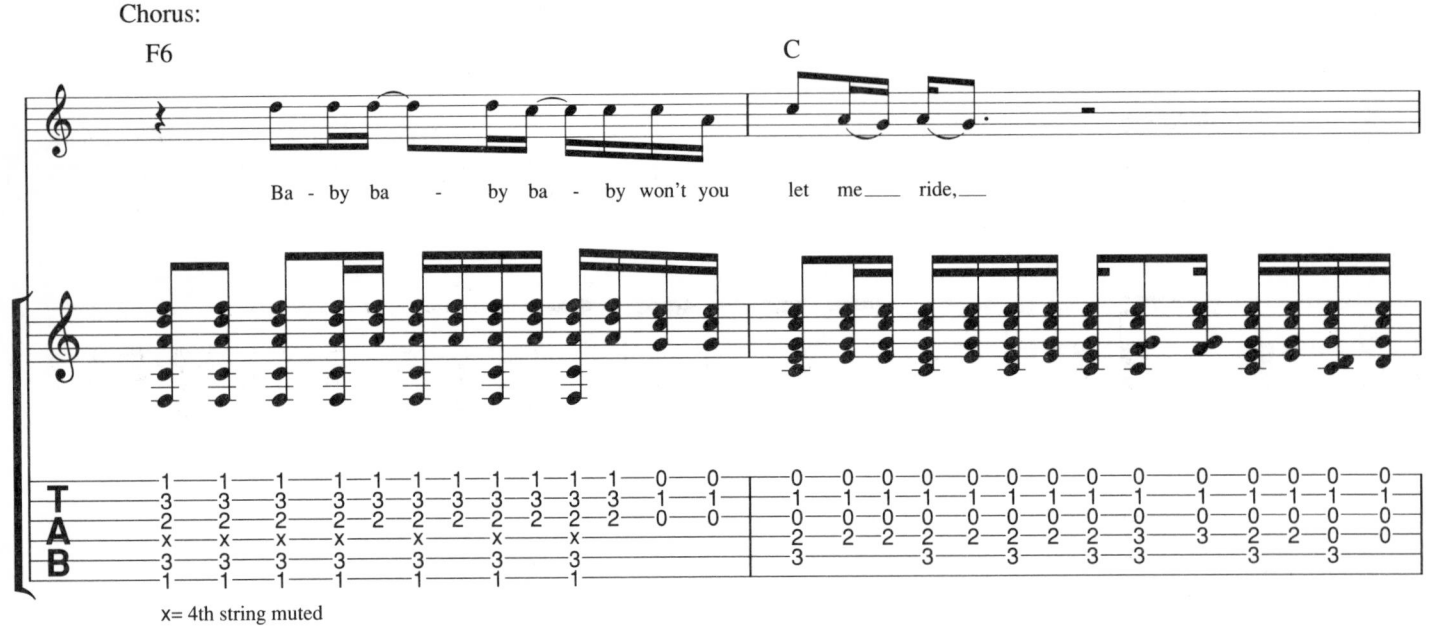

Ba - by ba - by ba - by won't you let me ride,

x= 4th string muted

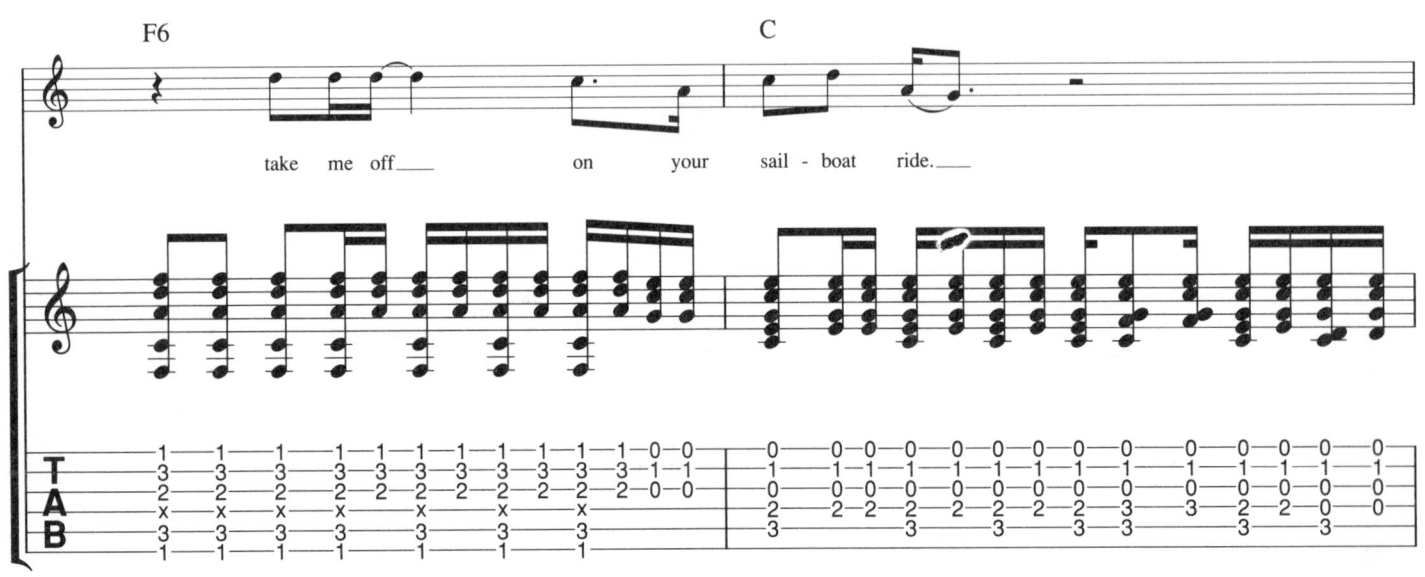

take me off___ on your sail - boat ride.___

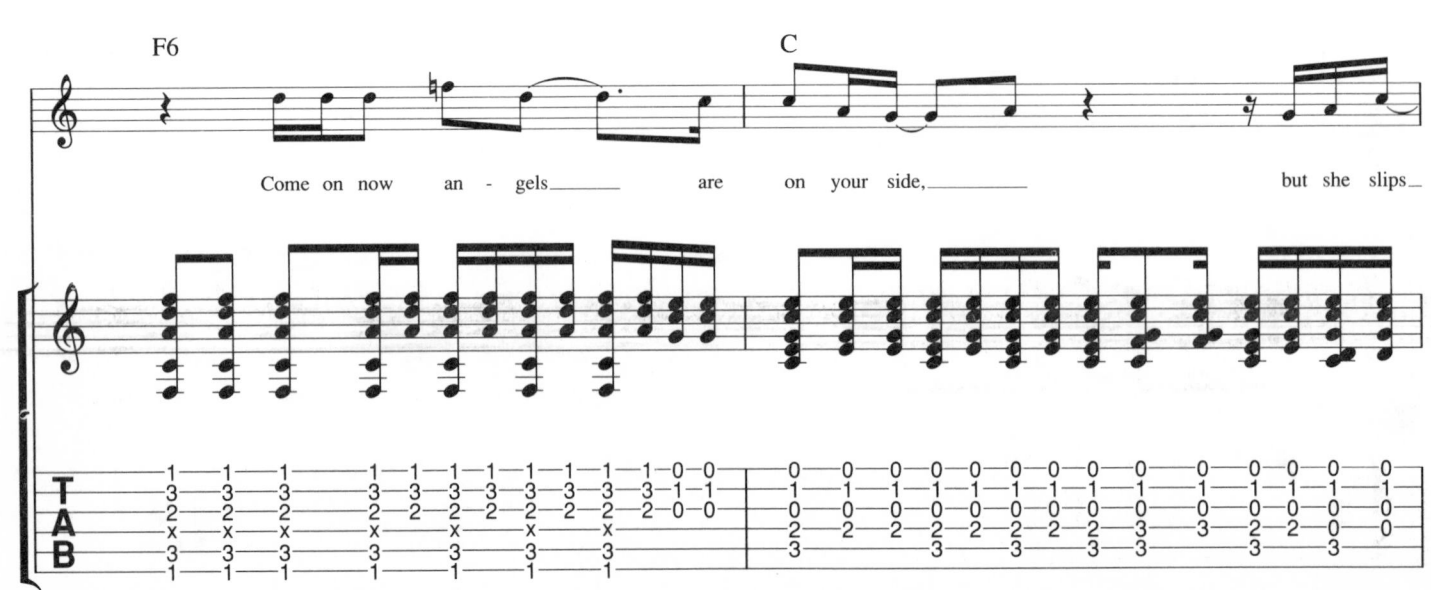

Come on now an - gels___ are on your side,___ but she slips___

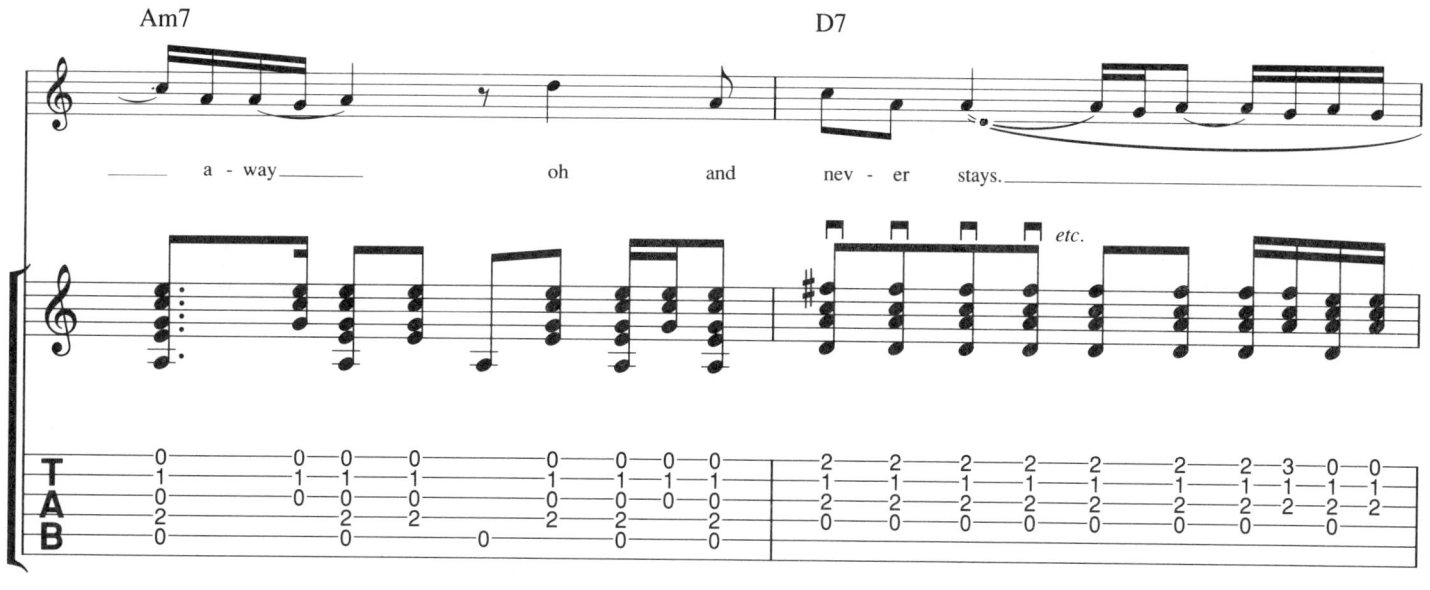

a - way   oh   and   nev - er   stays.

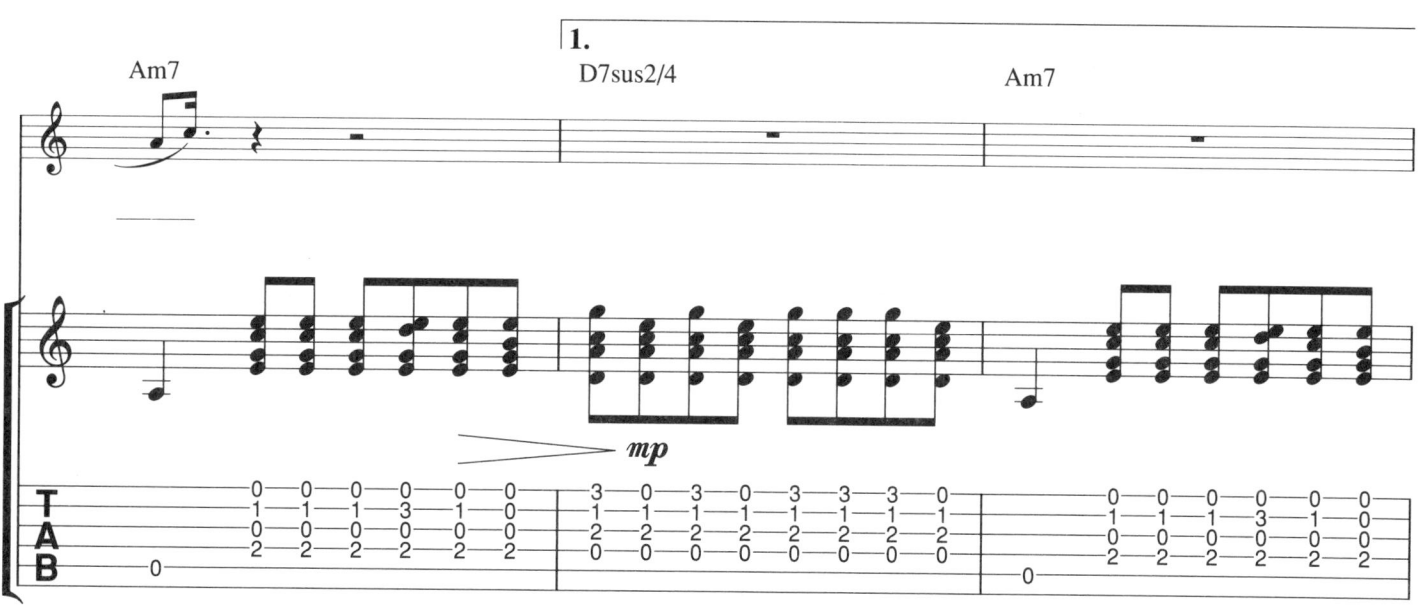

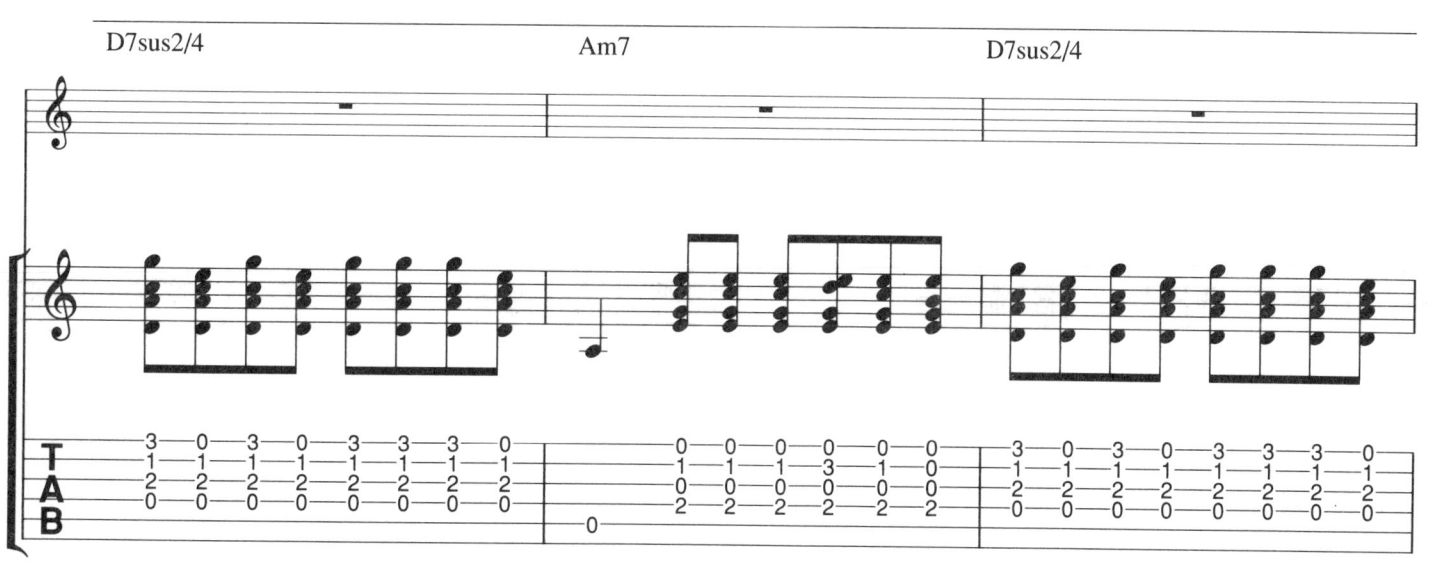

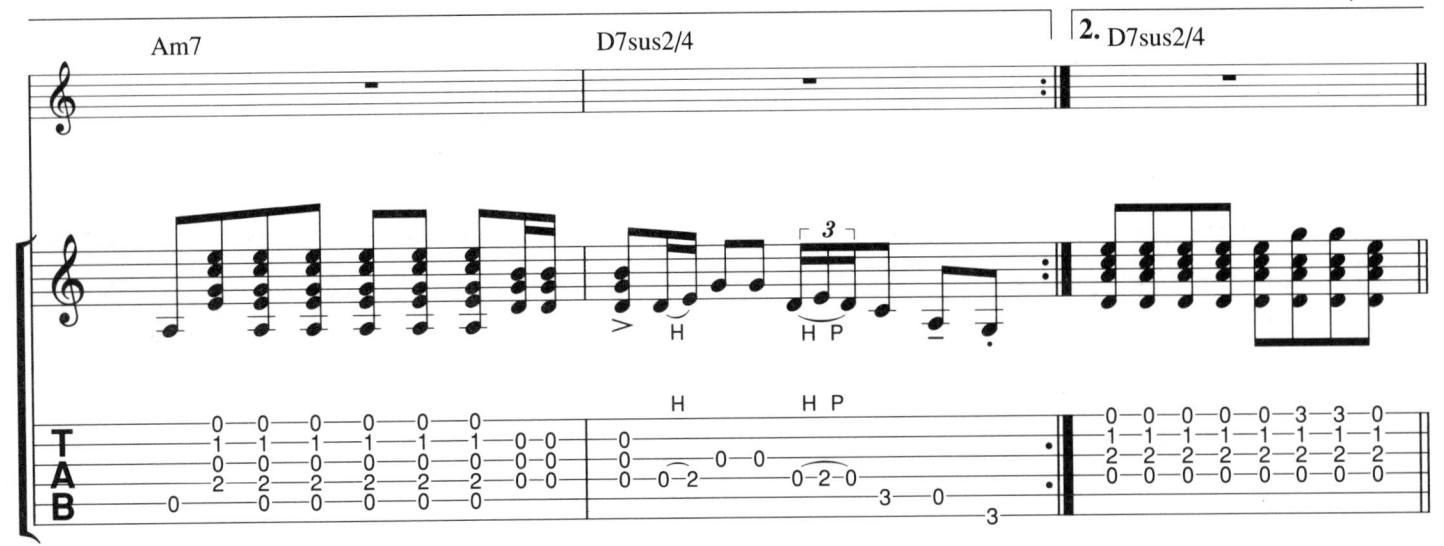

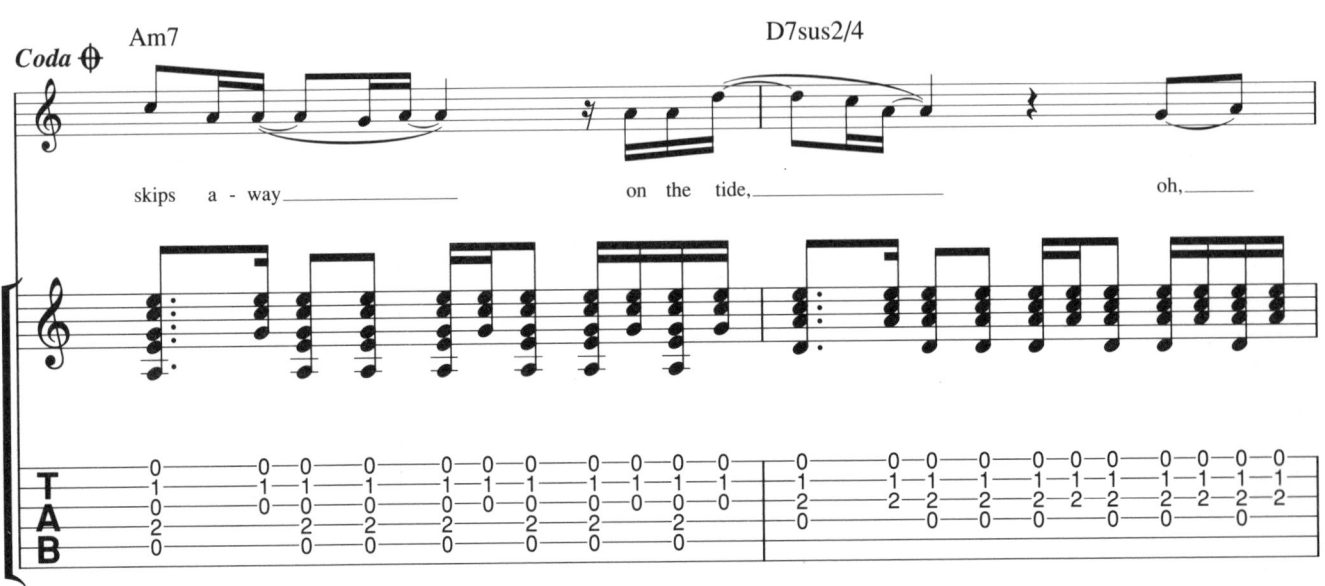

skips a - way_____ on the tide,_____ oh,_____

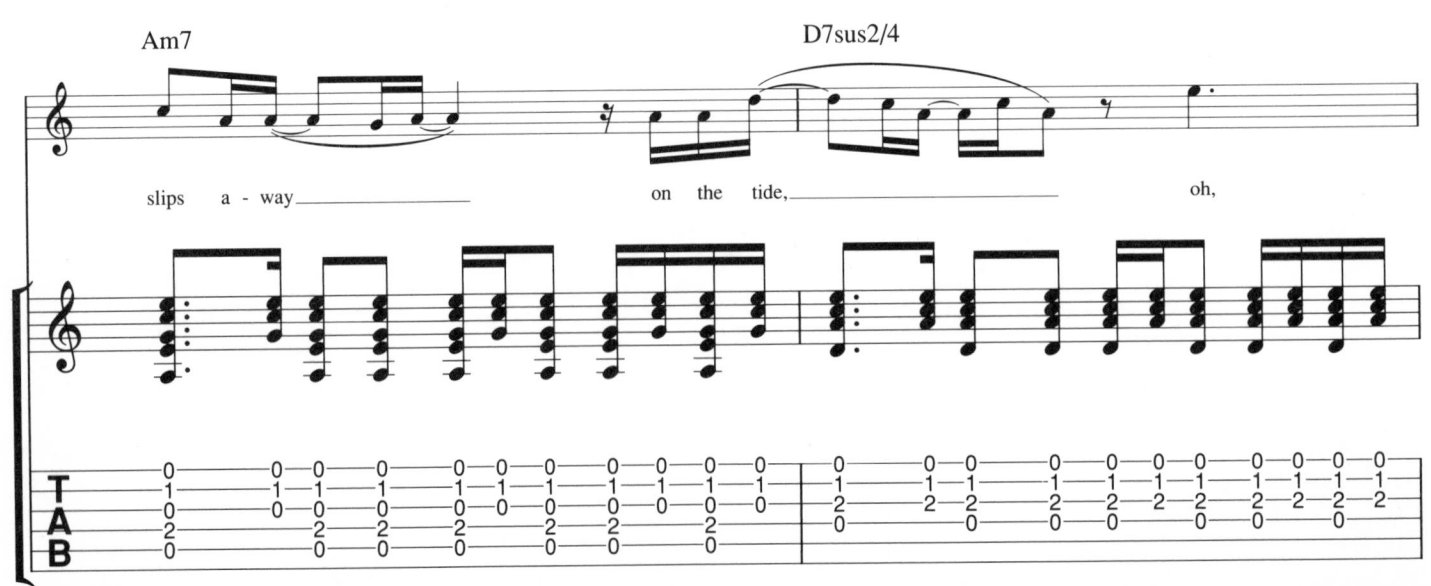

slips a - way_____ on the tide,_____ oh,

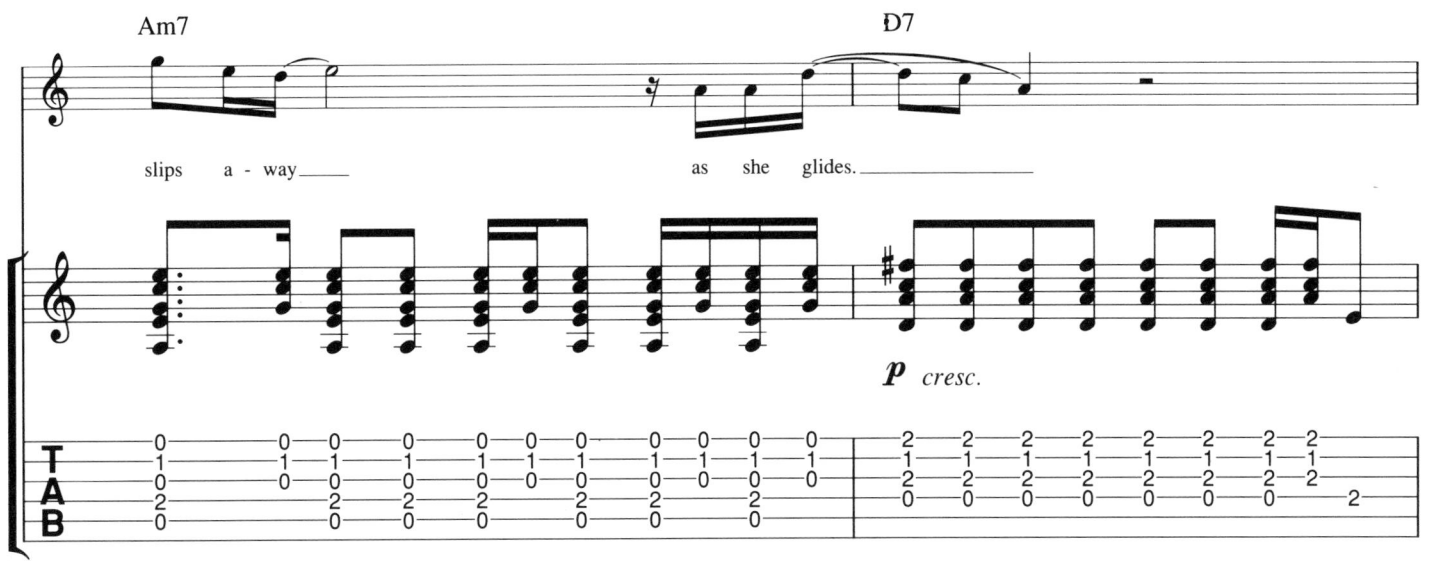

slips a - way_____ as she glides._____

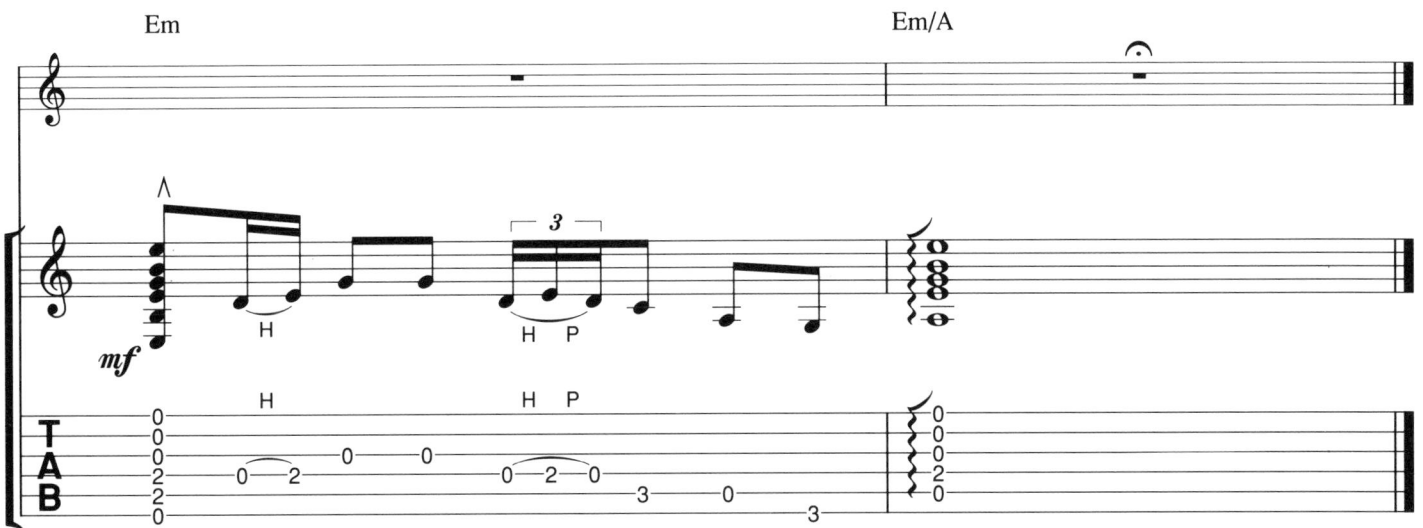

Verse 2:
Like mercury gliding
A silver teardrop that falls
And I can hold on
Through my fingers she's gone.
At the foot of the mountain
Such a long way to climb
How will I ever get up there?
Though I know I must try.

has my fire really gone out?

words & music by paul weller

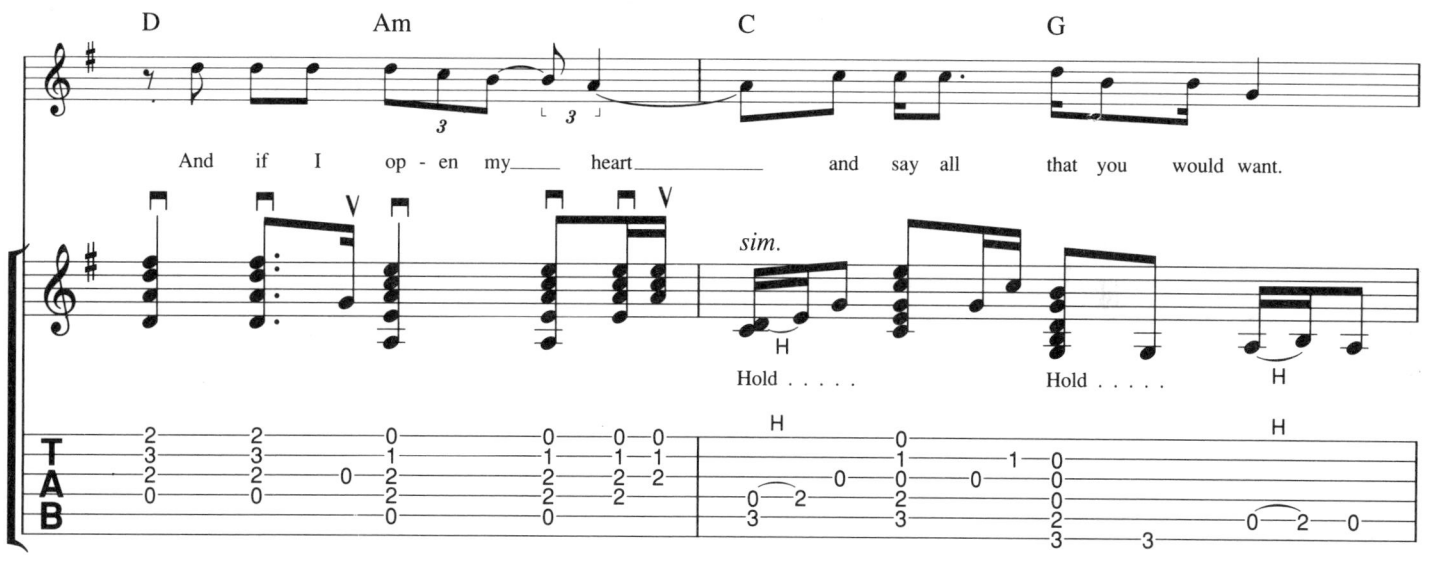

And if I op - en my____ heart_____ and say all that you would want.

Hold . . . . .   Hold . . . . .

To Coda ⊕

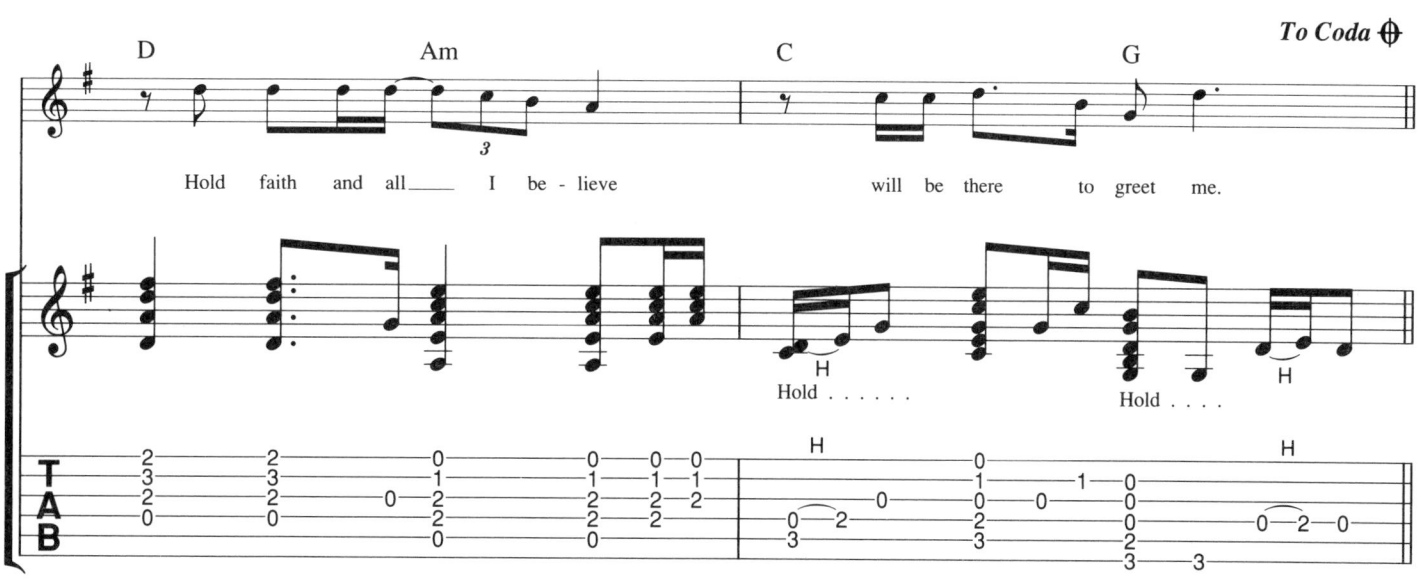

Hold faith and all____ I be - lieve will be there to greet me.

Hold . . . . . .   Hold . . . .

E♭maj7   Dm7   G

And put an end____ to all____ your doubts,____

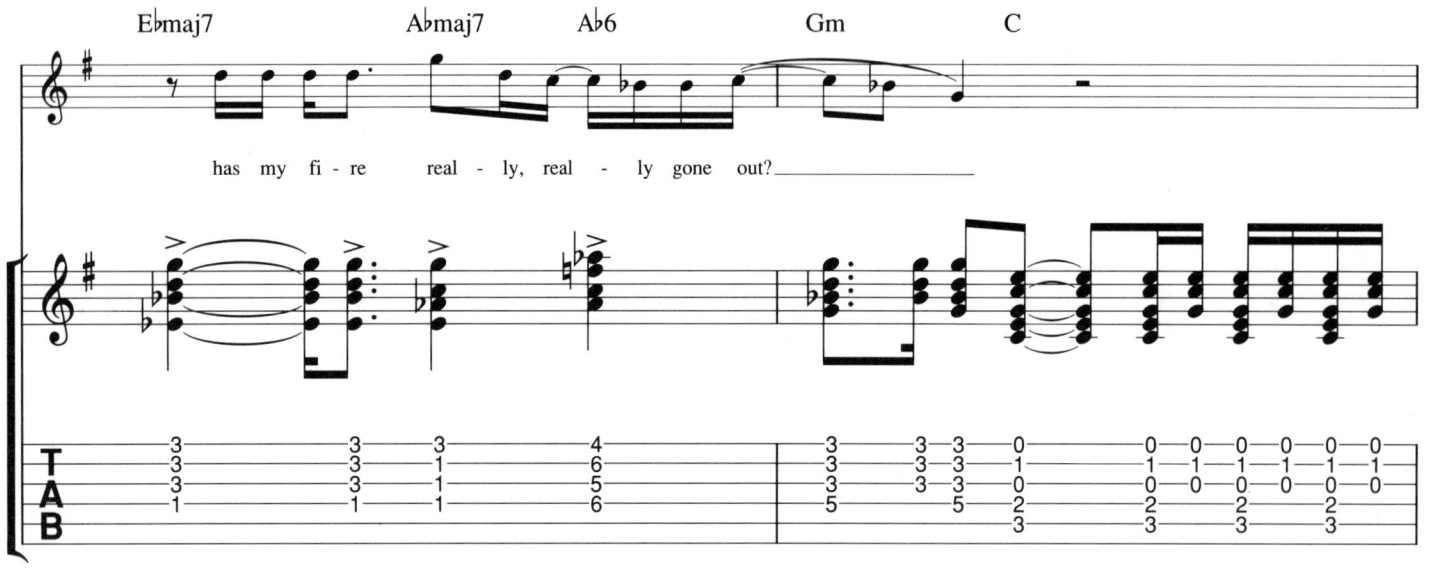

has my fi - re real - ly, real - ly gone out?_____

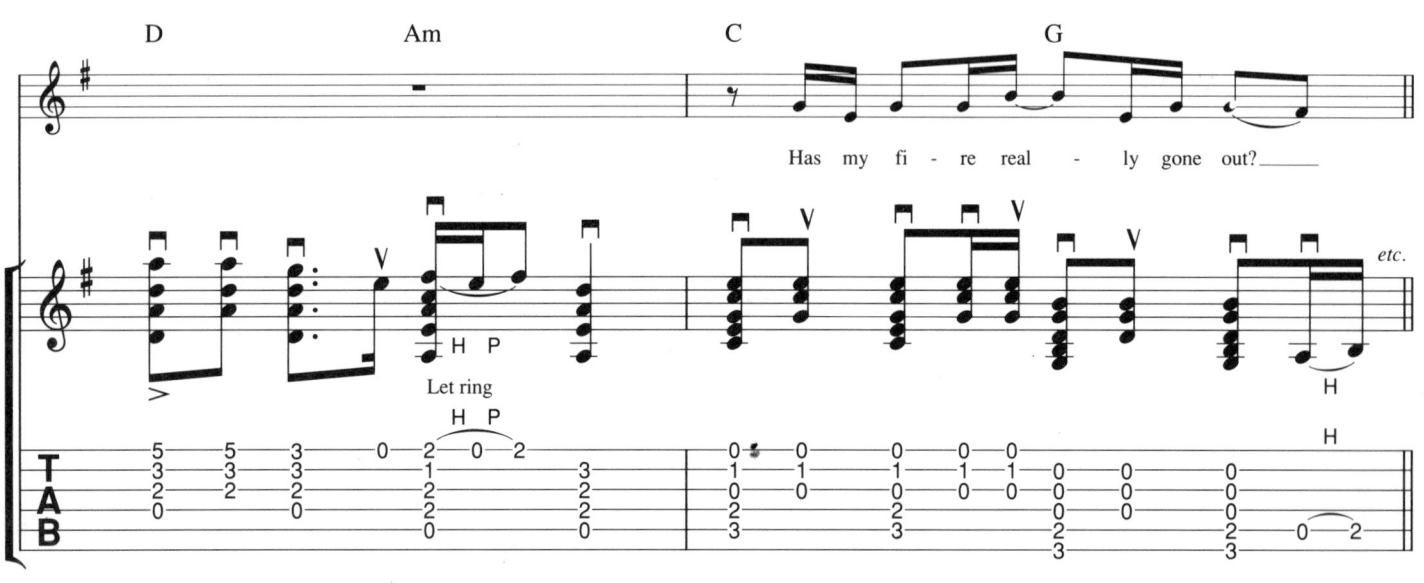

Has my fi - re real - ly gone out?_____

Verse:

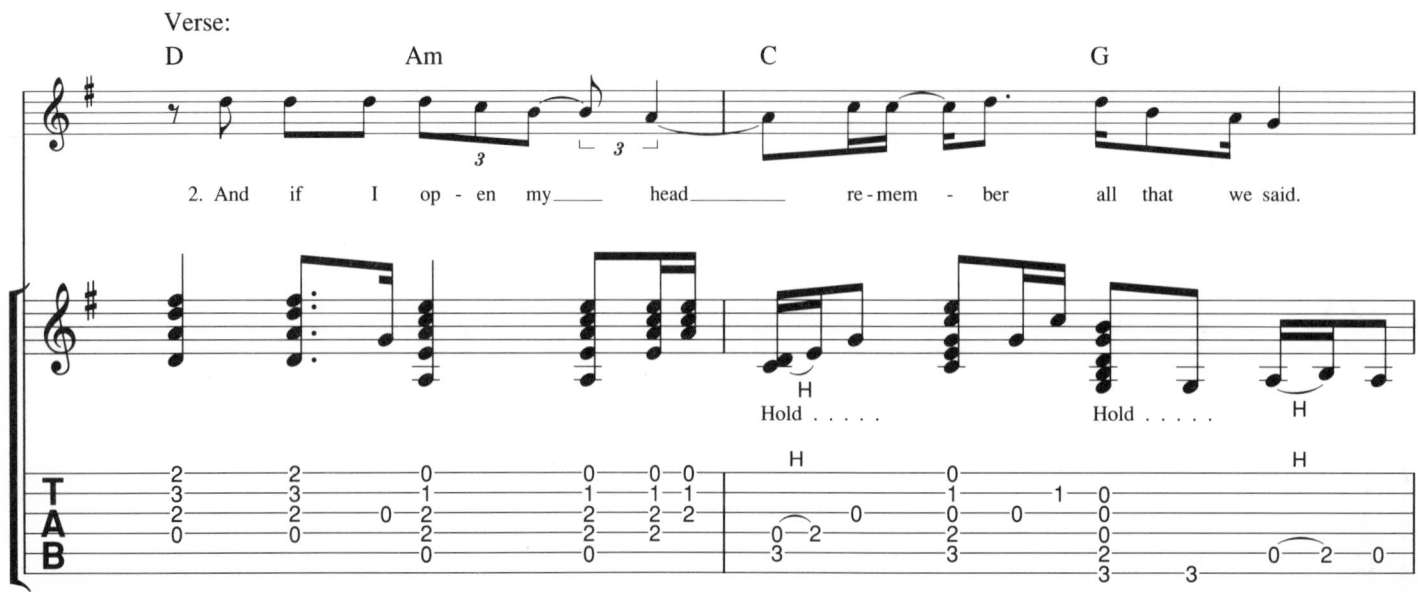

2. And if I op - en my____ head____ re - mem - ber all that we said.

Hey ba - by what will you find com - in' down___ to meet you?
Hold . . . . . Hold . . . H

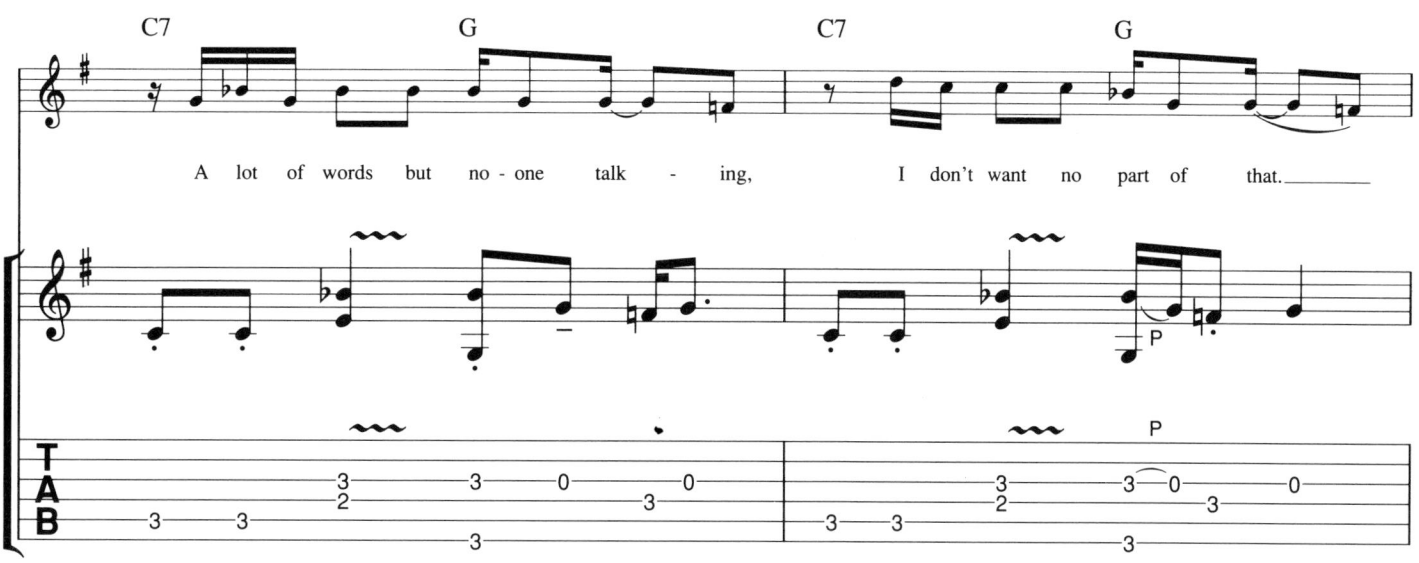

A lot of words but no - one talk - ing, I don't want no part of that.___

Some - thing real is what I'm seek - ing, one clear voice in the wil - der - ness._____

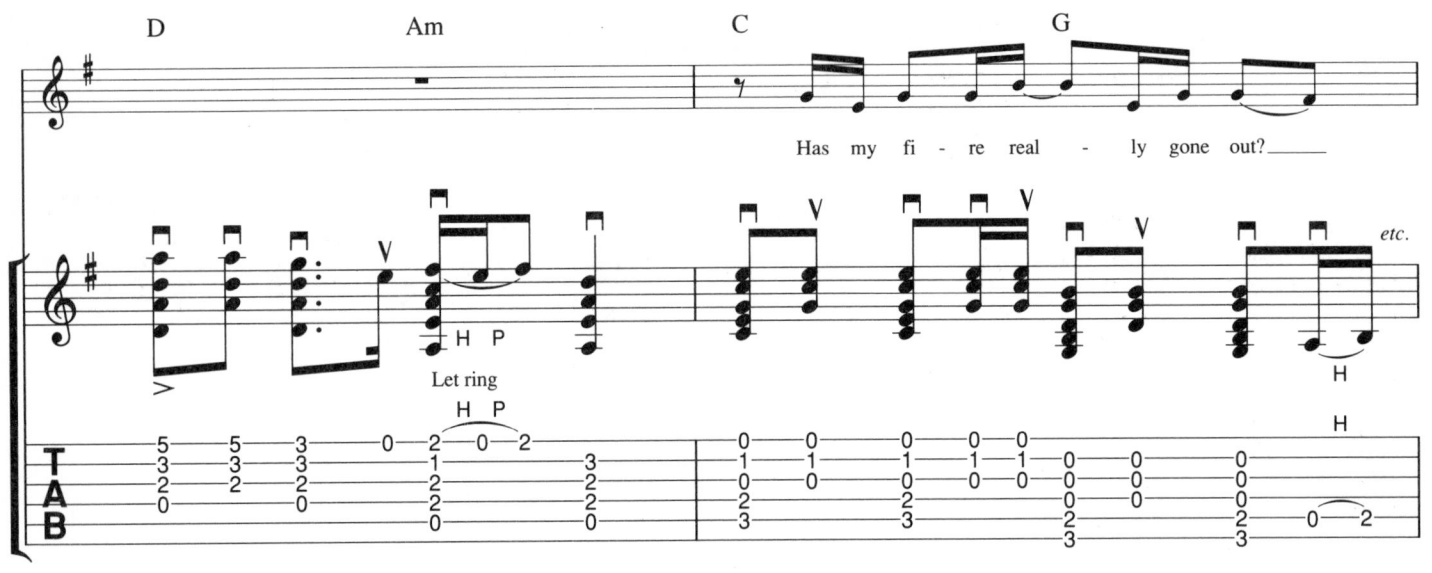

Has my fi - re real - ly gone out?

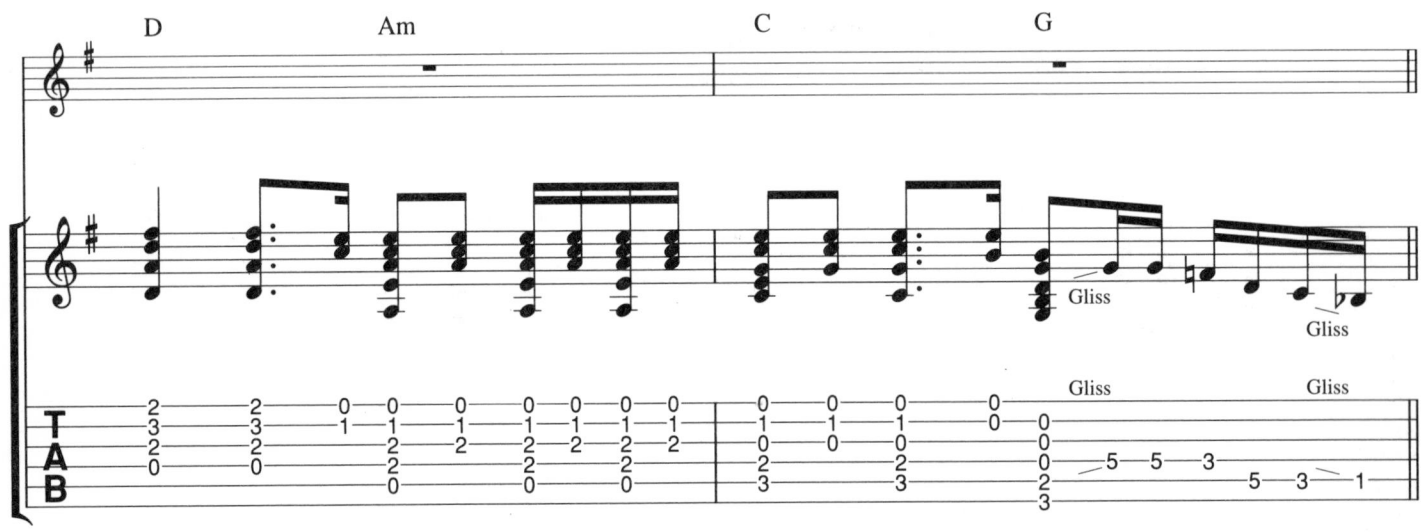

Put an end to all your doubts,

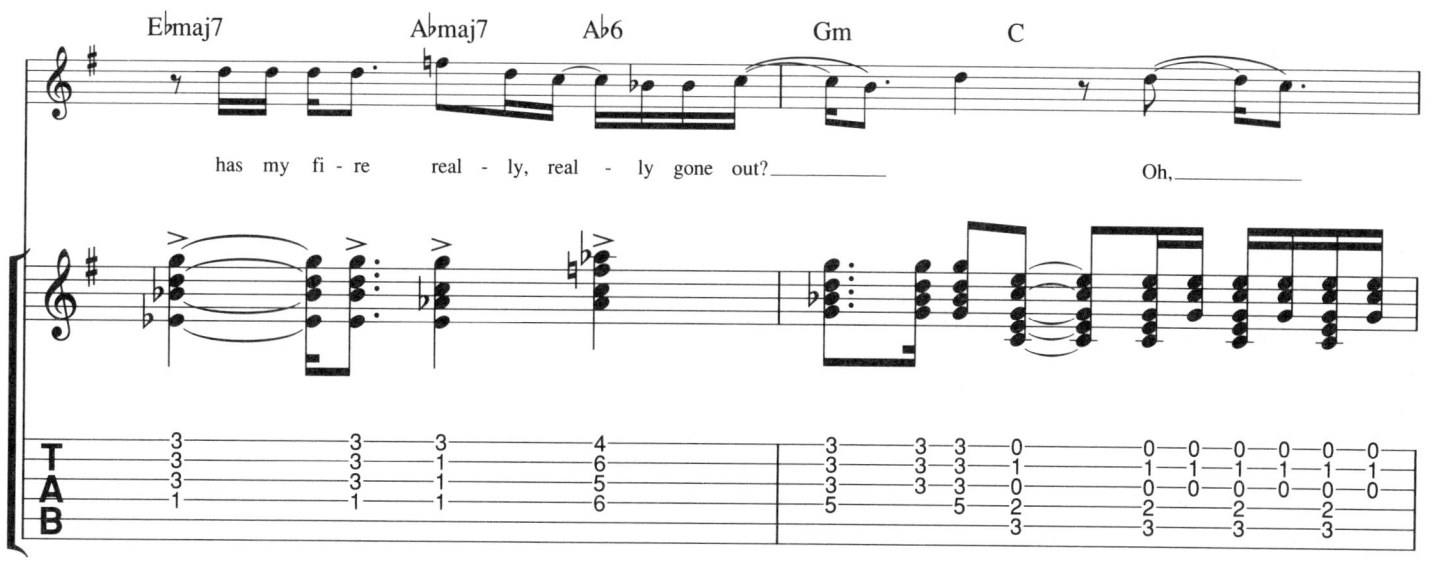

has my fi - re real - ly, real - ly gone out? _____ Oh, _____

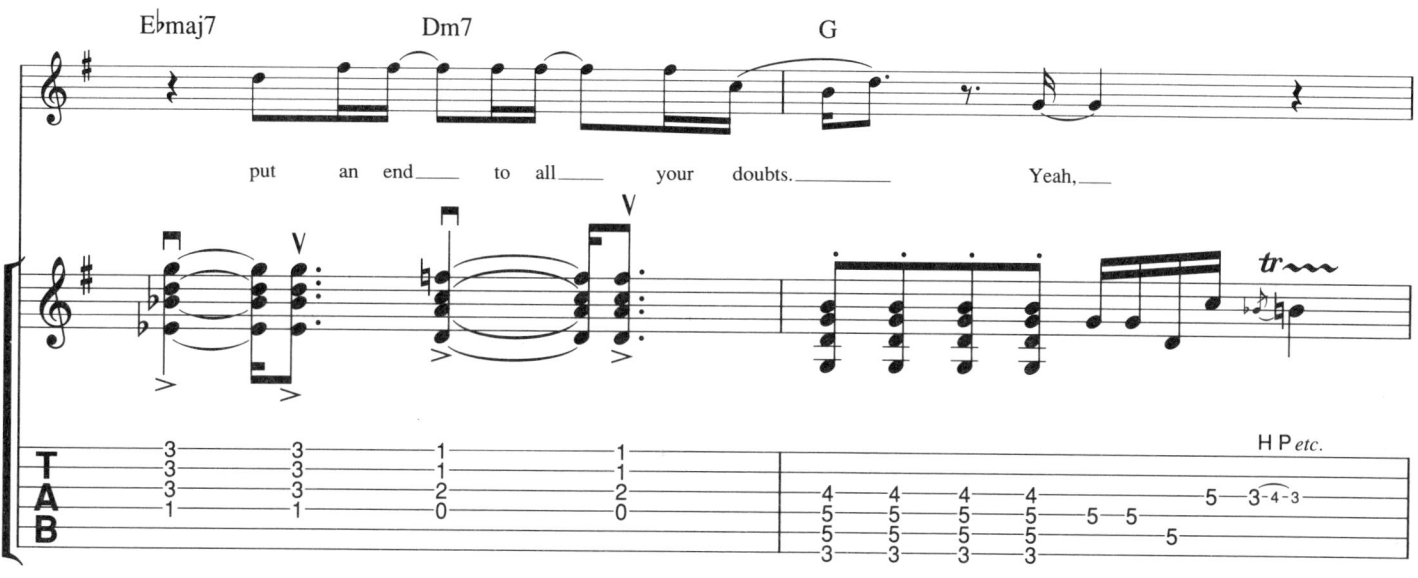

put an end _____ to all _____ your doubts. _____ Yeah, _____

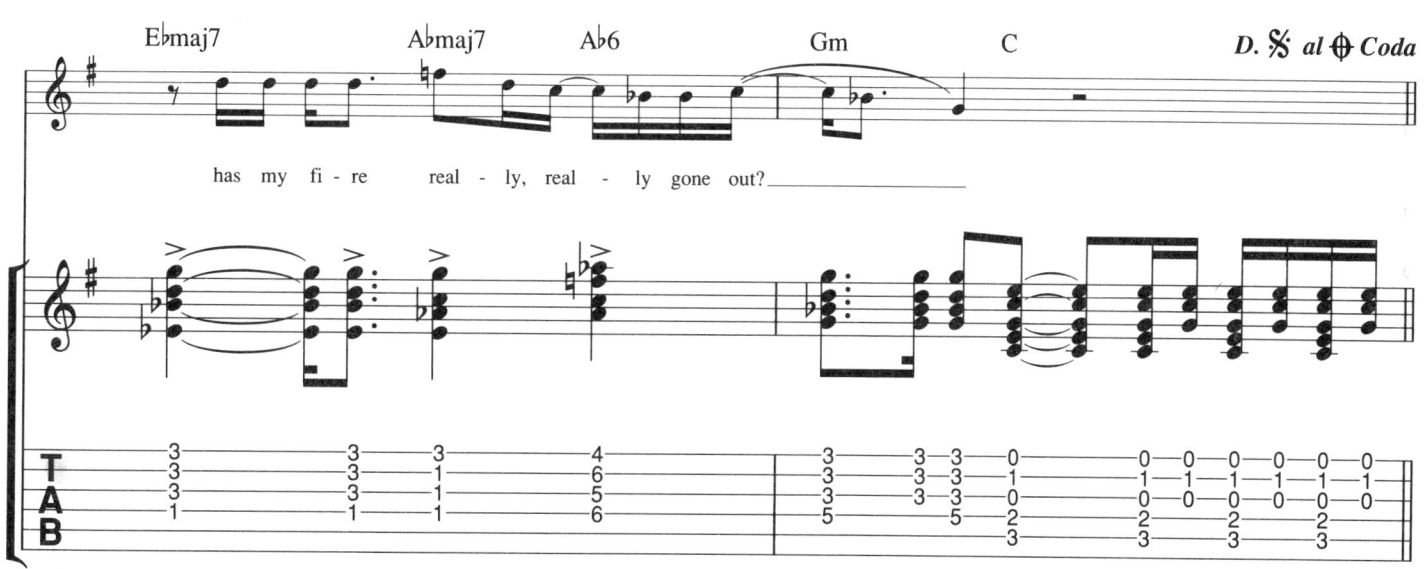

has my fi - re real - ly, real - ly gone out? _____

D. %. al ⊕ Coda

Some-thing real is what I'm seek - ing,

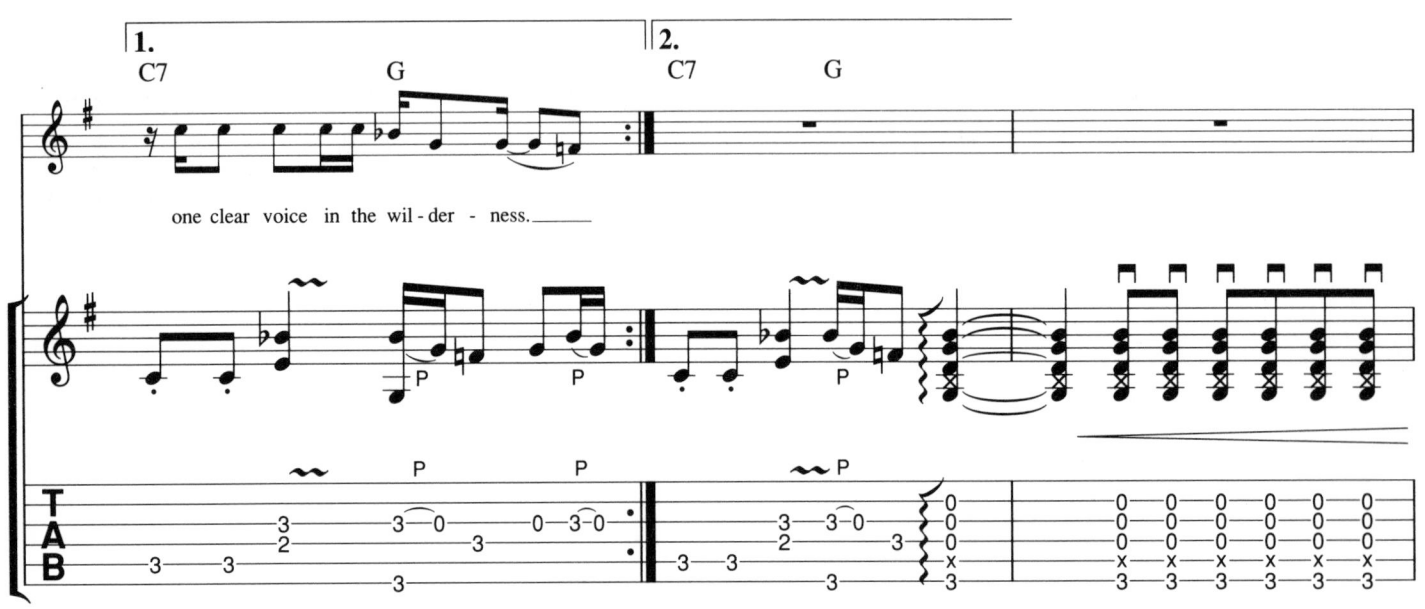

one clear voice in the wil - der - ness._____

Drum solo:

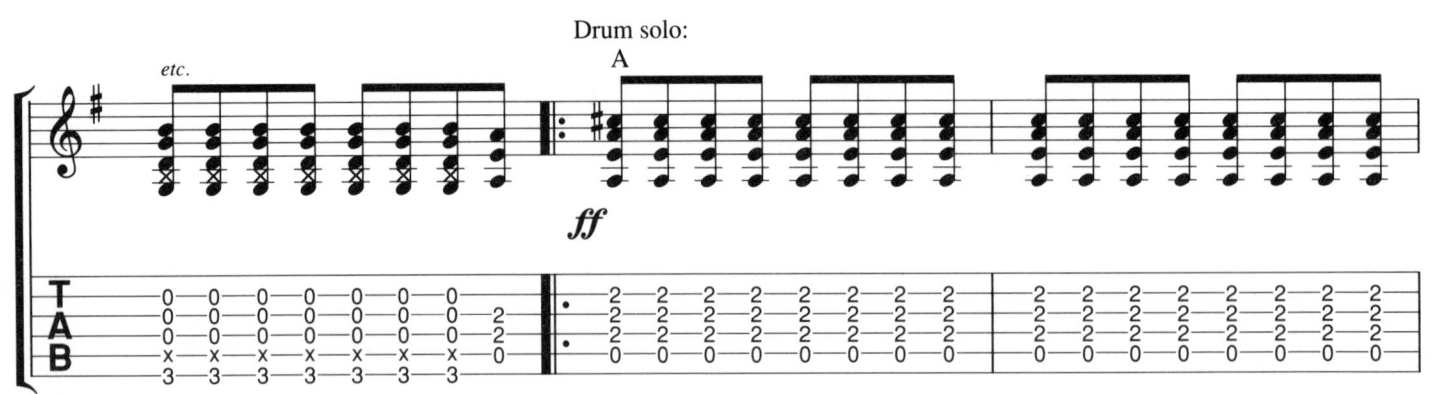

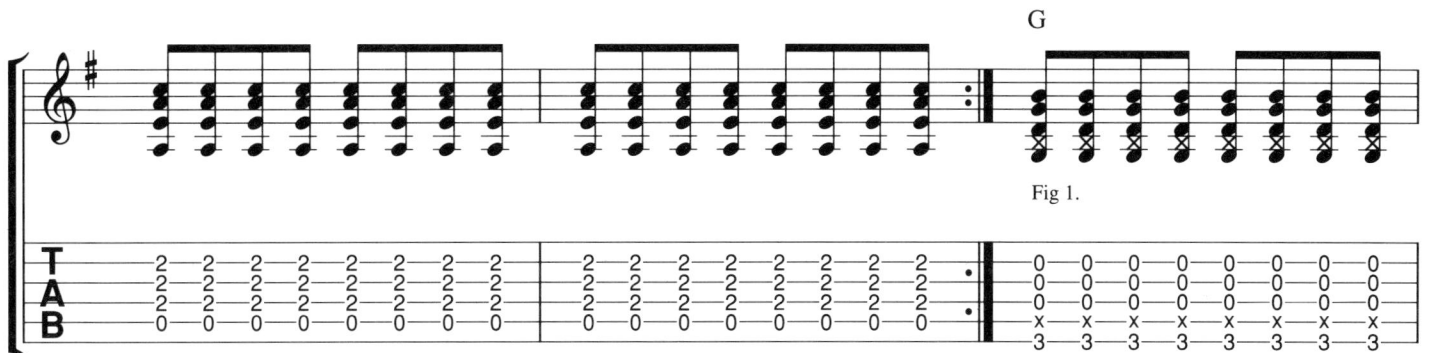

G

Fig 1.

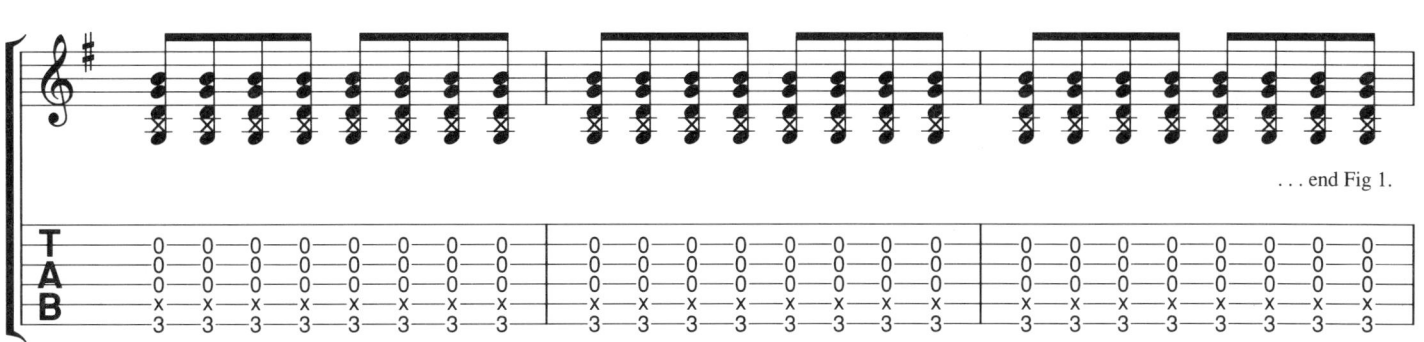

. . . end Fig 1.

G

w/Fig 1.   Hold . . . . . .   sim.

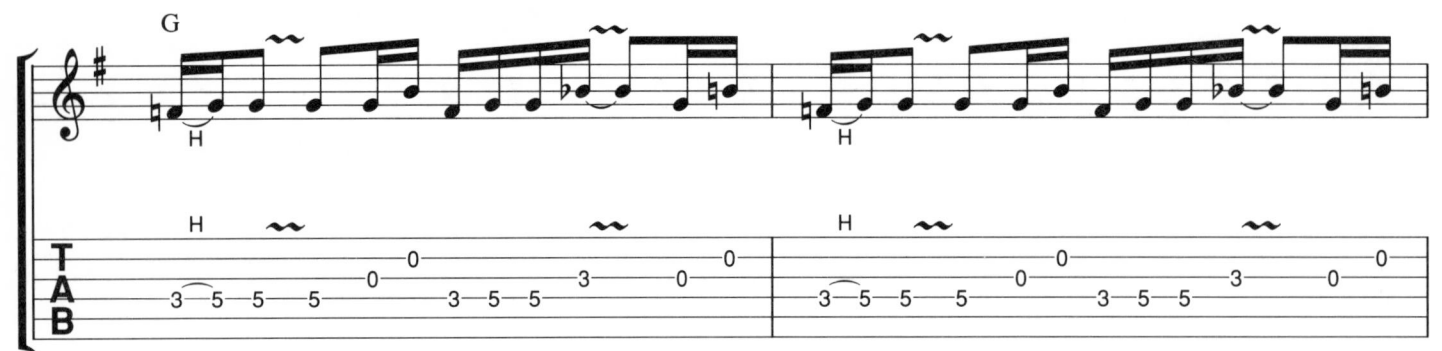

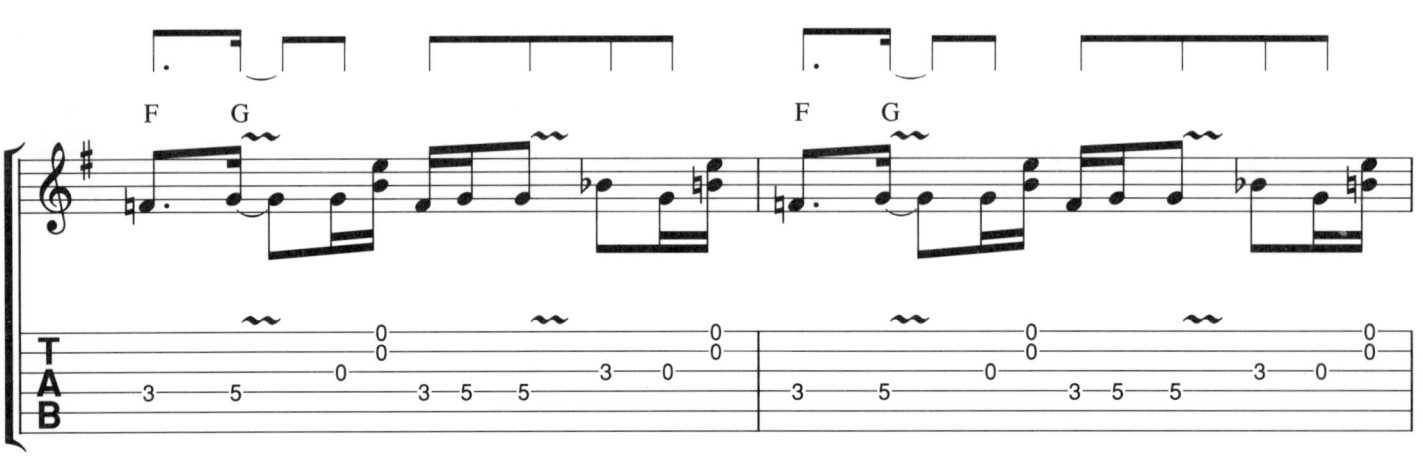

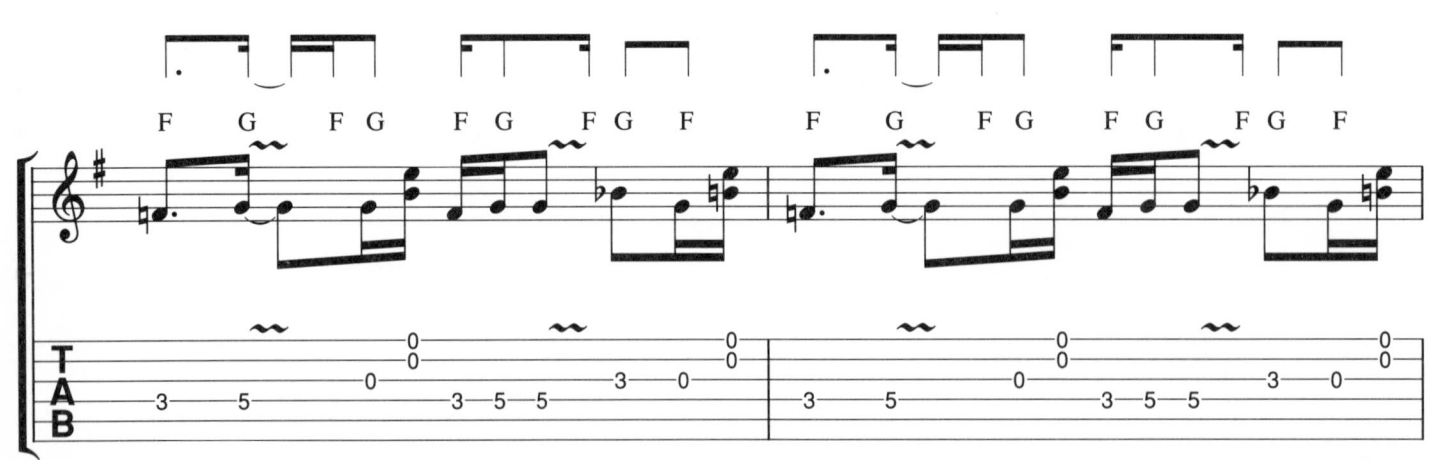

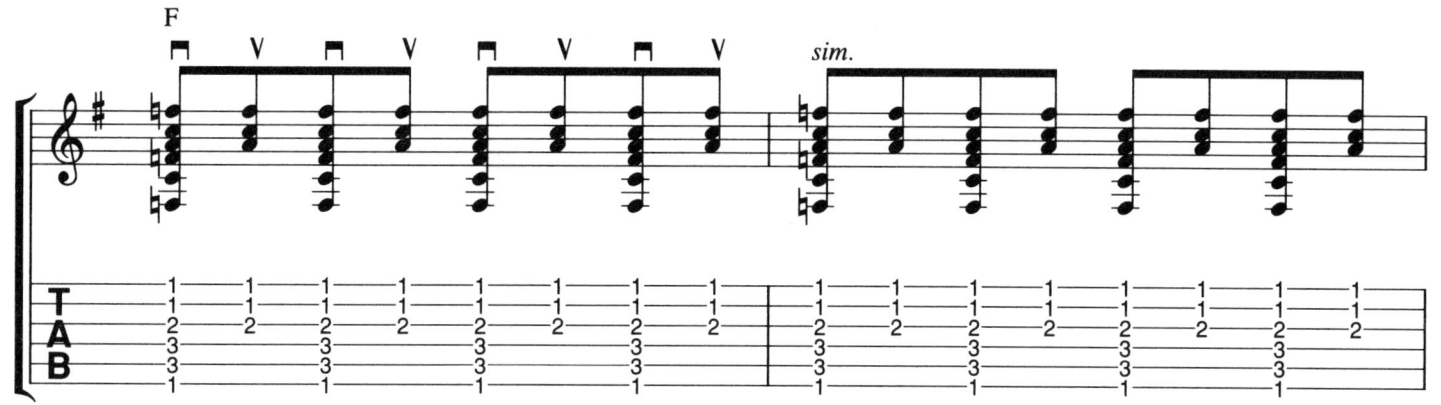

into tomorrow

words & music by paul weller

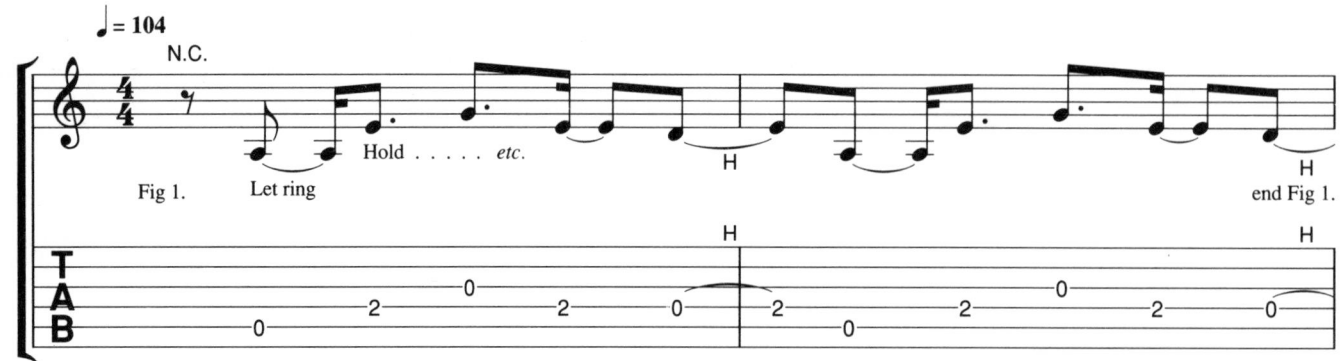

◻ = downstroke   V = upstroke

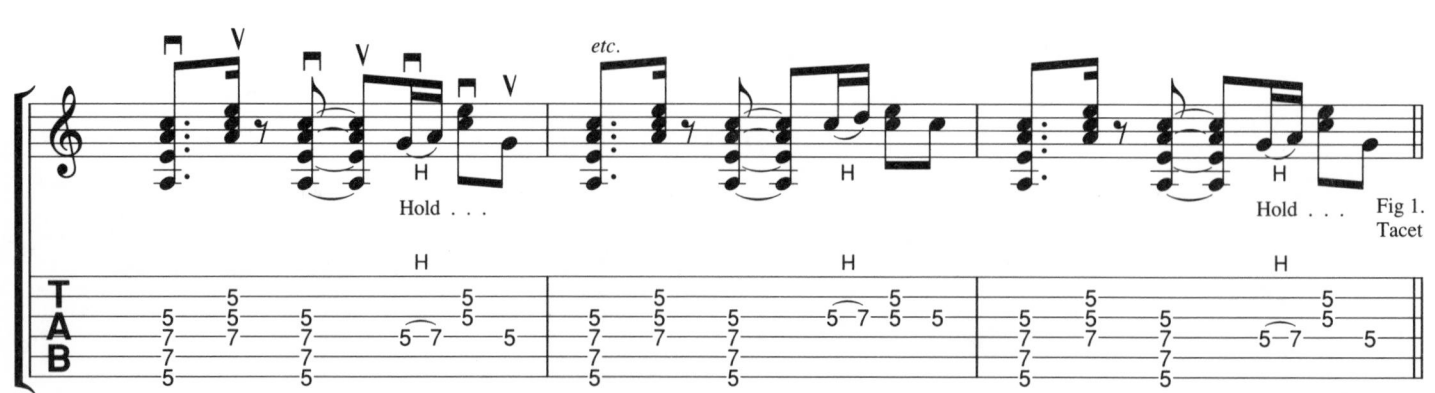

Verse:

1. In-to the mists__of time__and space__ where we have__no say__ o-ver date_____ and place__ oh, yeah.__

Fig 2.   Hold . . .   Hold . . .
                                    end Fig 2.

_____ Don't get em-bar-rassed if it hap-pens a lot,___ that you

Hold . . .

don't know how__ you start-ed or where____ you're gon-a stop,___ oh,__ yeah. And

Hold . . .   Hold . . .

C   D7sus4   Am

if at times it seems in - sane,   all the tears and search - ing,   turn-ing on your joy to pain

D7sus4   Fmaj7

in pur - suit of learn - ing,   buy a dream and hide a - way,

G6   Amadd9

can't es - cape the sor - row,   your mo - jo will have no ef - fect

and minds⎯ ah, yeah,⎯ yeah,⎯yeah, yeah.⎯ And if at times⎯it seems⎯in - sane,⎯

Hold . . .

D7sus4

all the tears⎯ in search - ing,

Am

turn-ing all⎯your joy⎯ to pain⎯

D7sus4

in pur - suit⎯ of learn - ing,

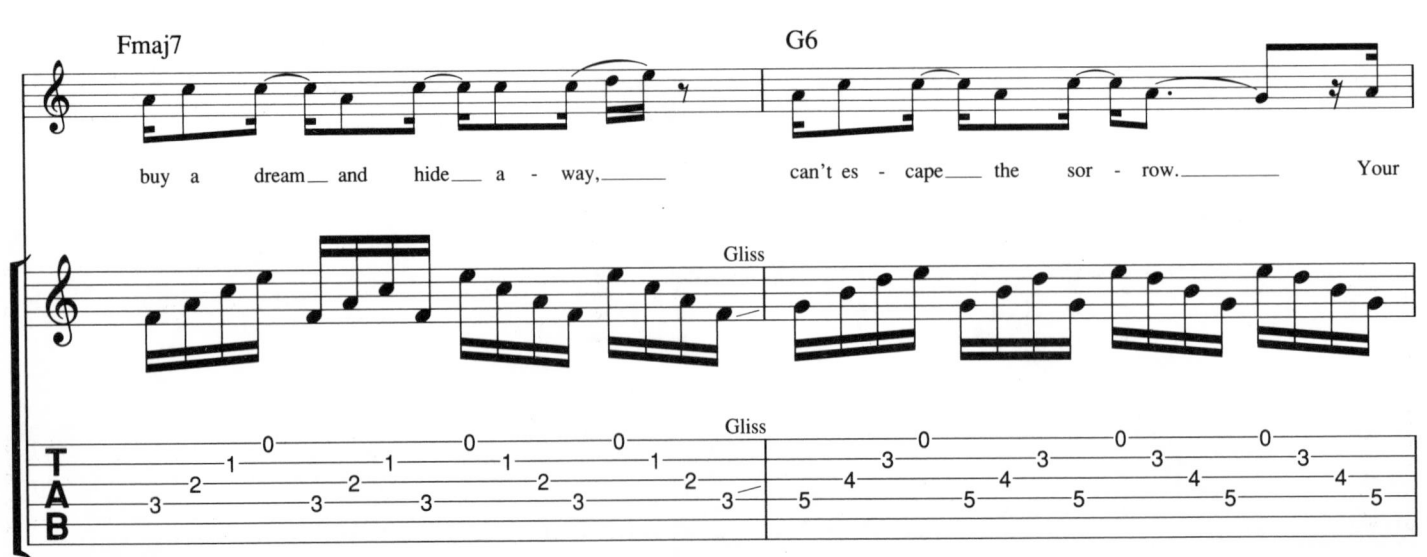

Fmaj7

buy a dream⎯ and hide⎯ a - way,⎯

G6

can't es - cape⎯ the sor - row.⎯ Your

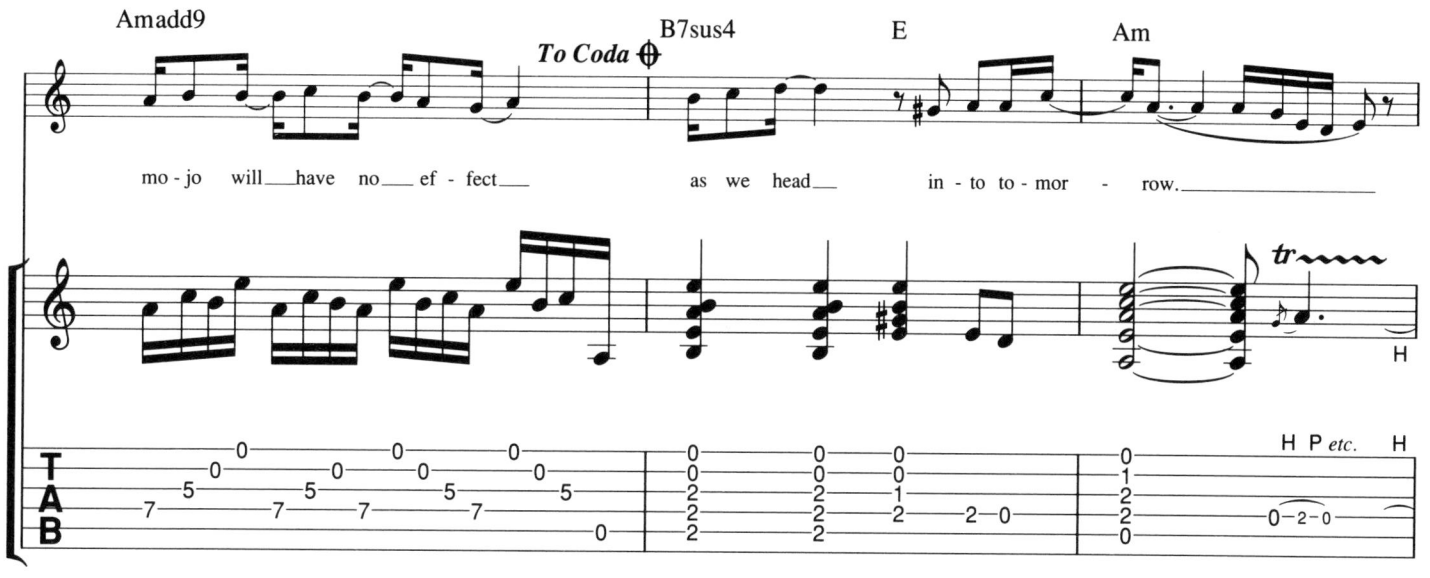

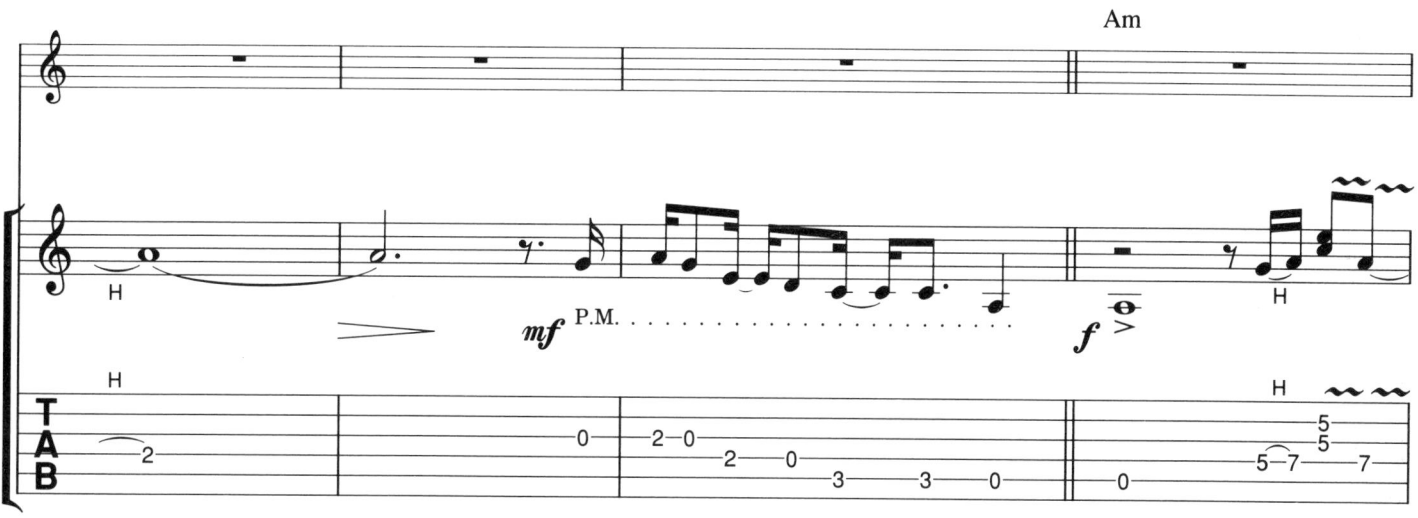

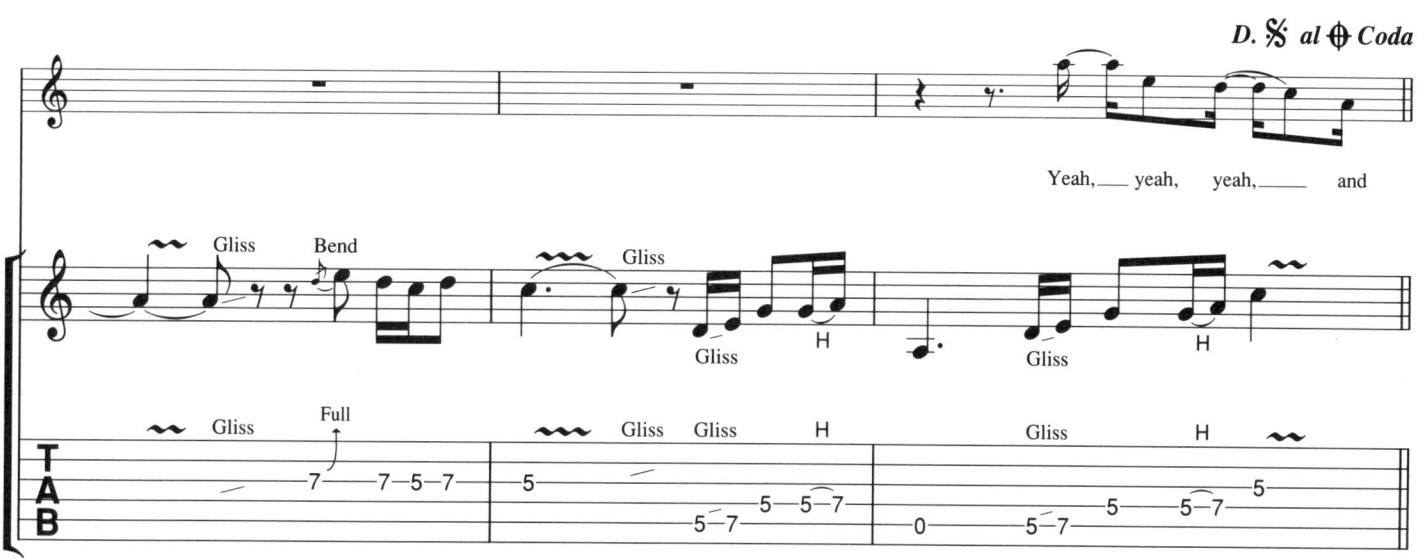

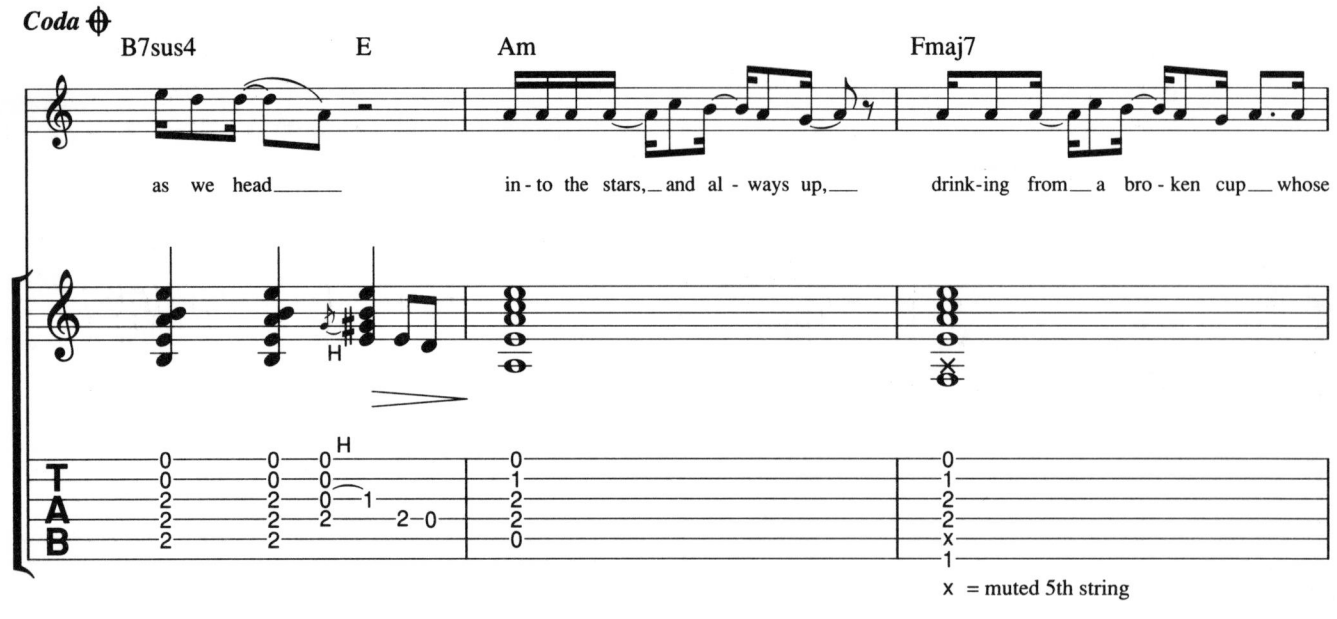

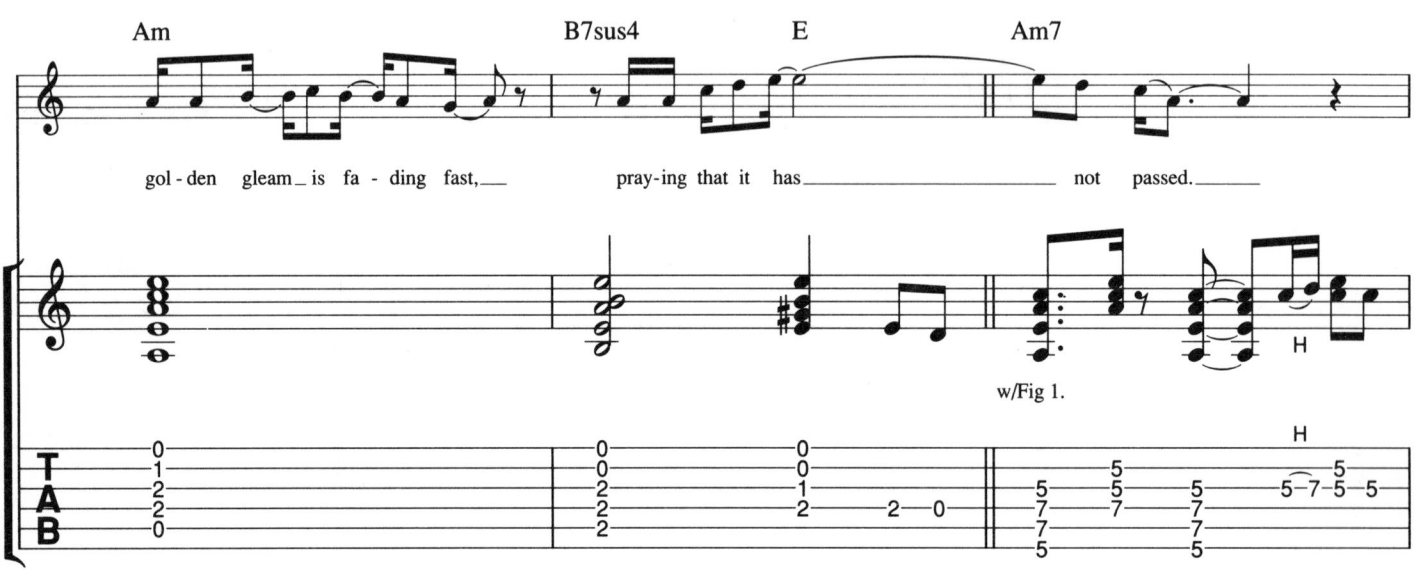

row, oh, yeah, in - to to - mor -

Hold . . .

Repeat to fade

row, oh, yeah, oh, in - to to - mor -

Hold . . .

out of the sinking

words & music by paul weller

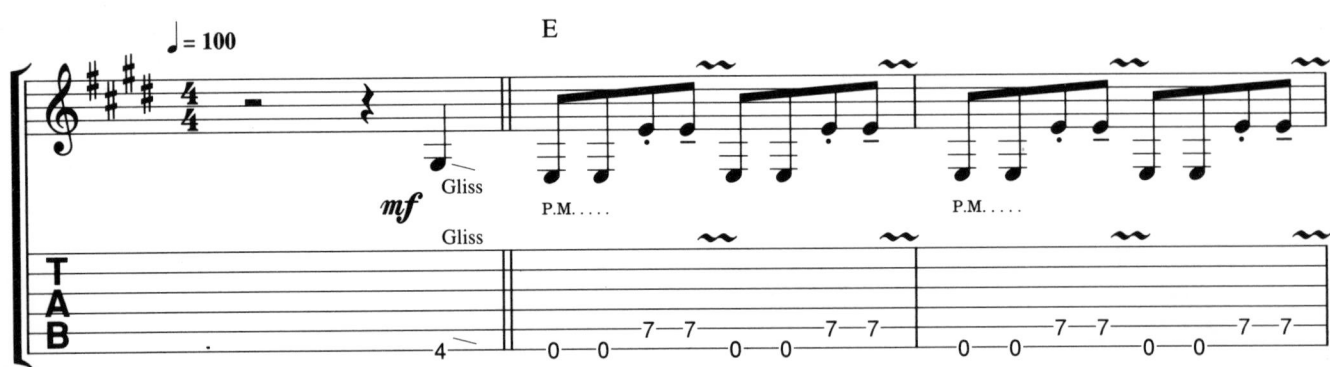

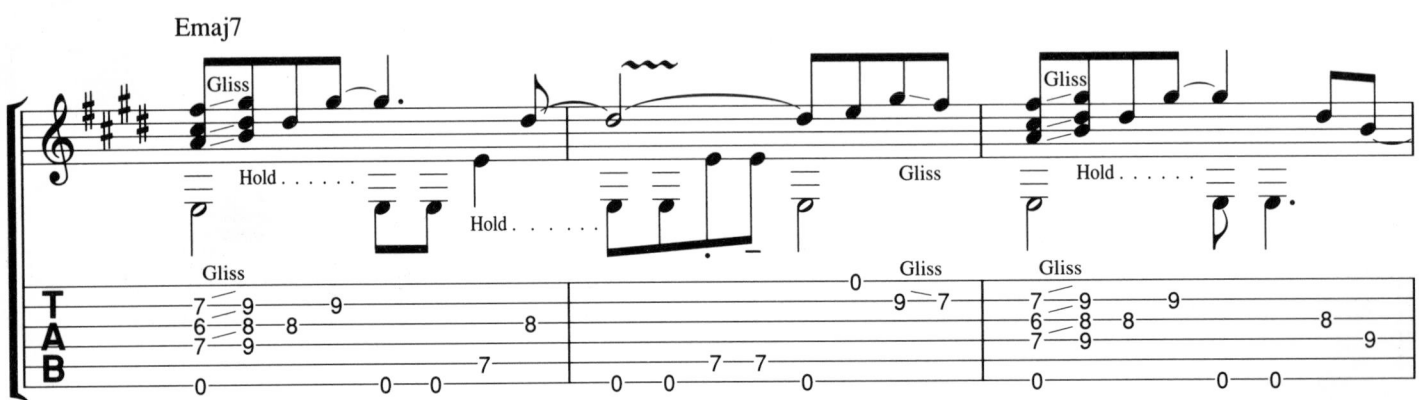

1. Past mid - nights____ hold,_____
See Block Lyrics for Verse 2 (𝄎)

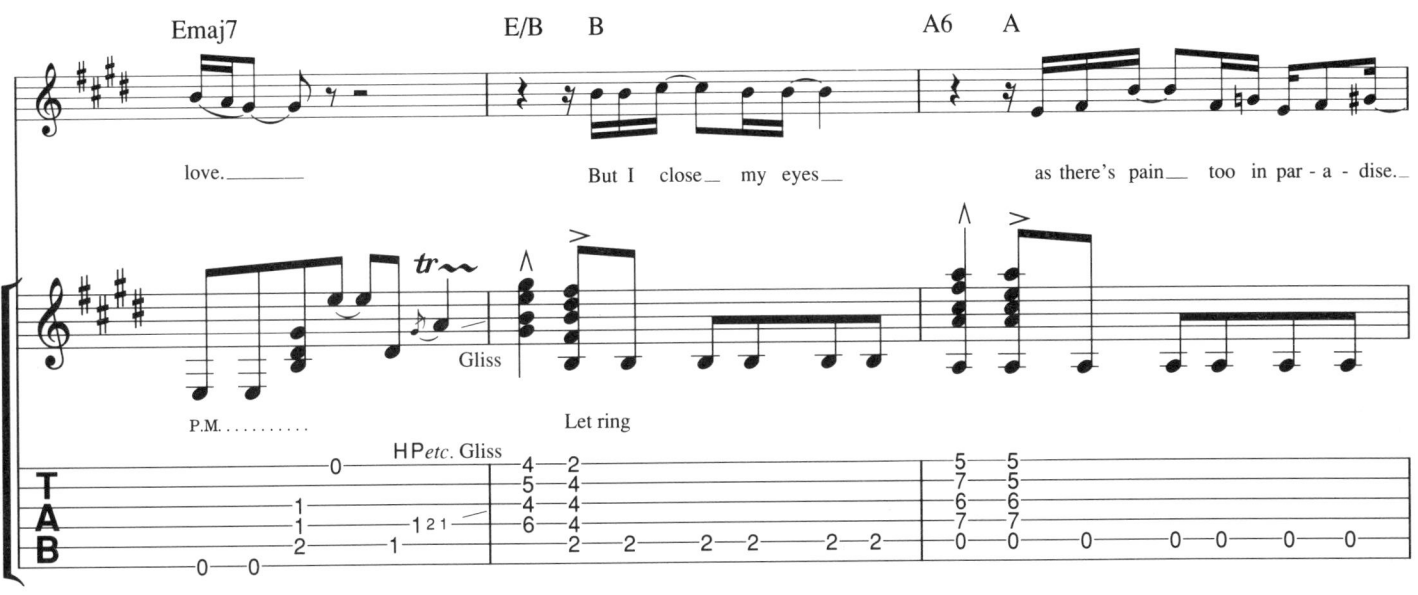

just____ what you're think-ing.____   Know__ I know it   yeah,___feel I'm sink - ing.

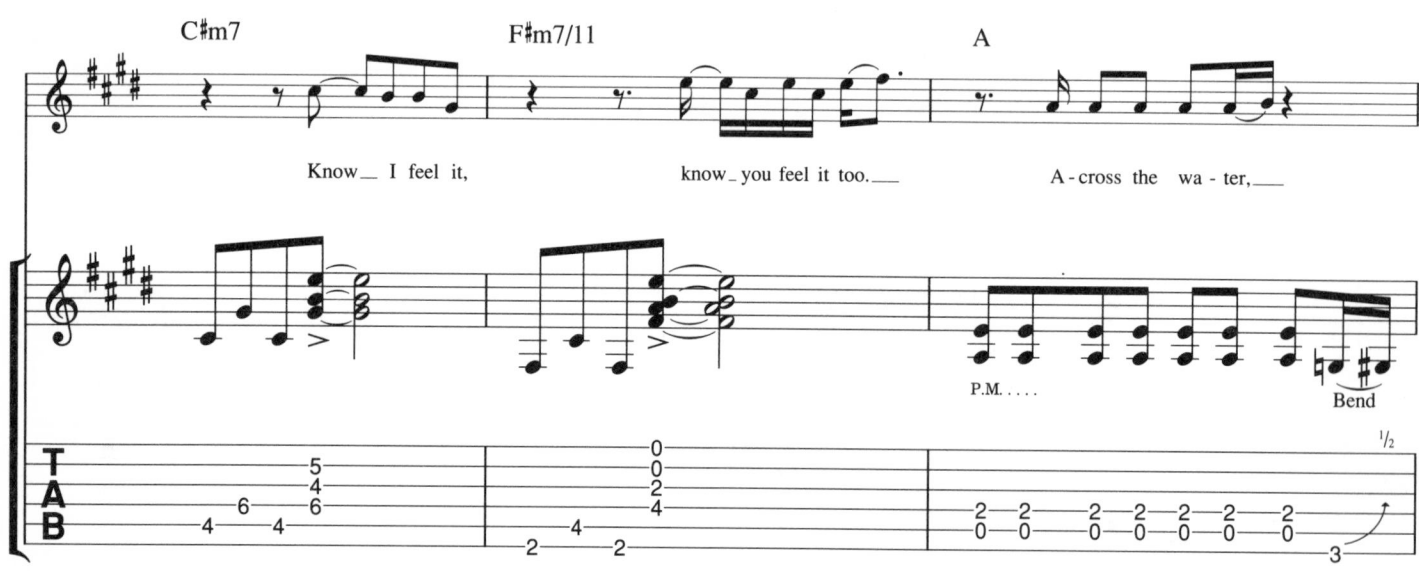

Know__ I feel it,   know__ you feel it too.____   A - cross the wa - ter,____

To Coda ⊕

there's a boat that____   will take us a - way.____

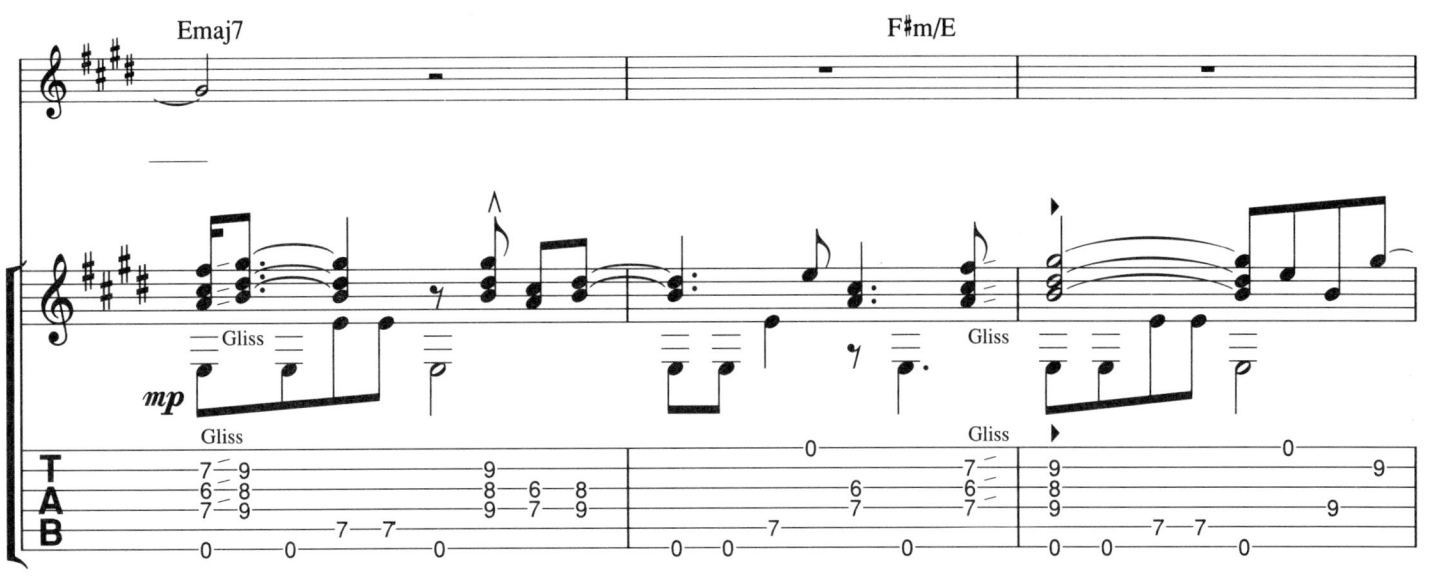

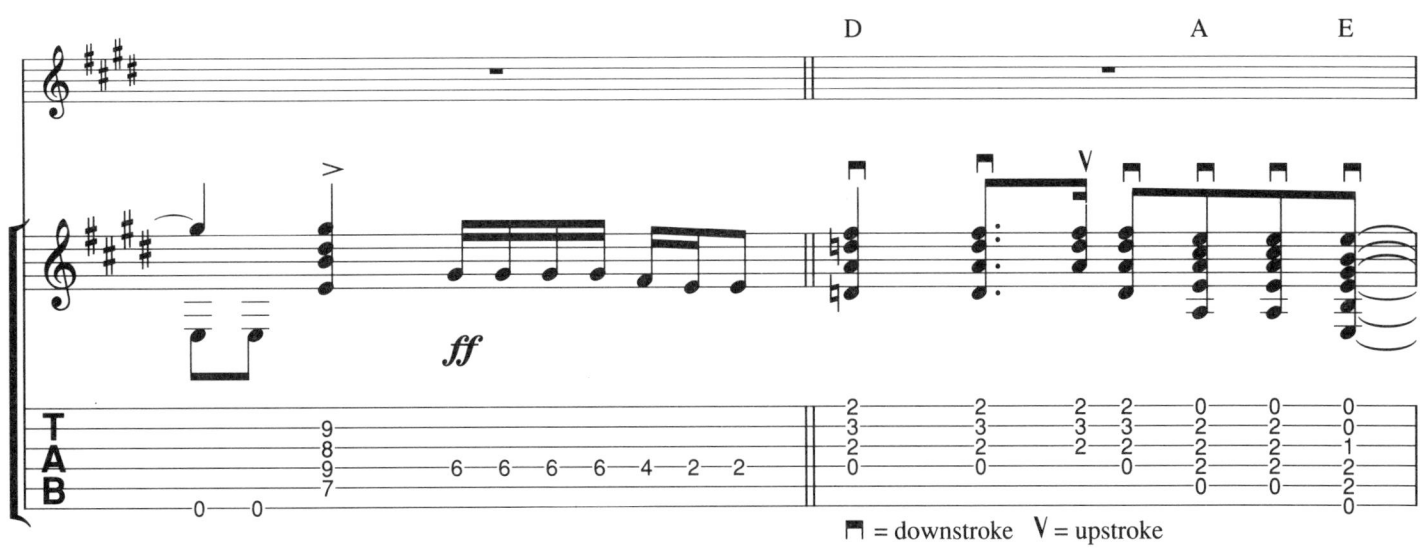

= downstroke   V = upstroke

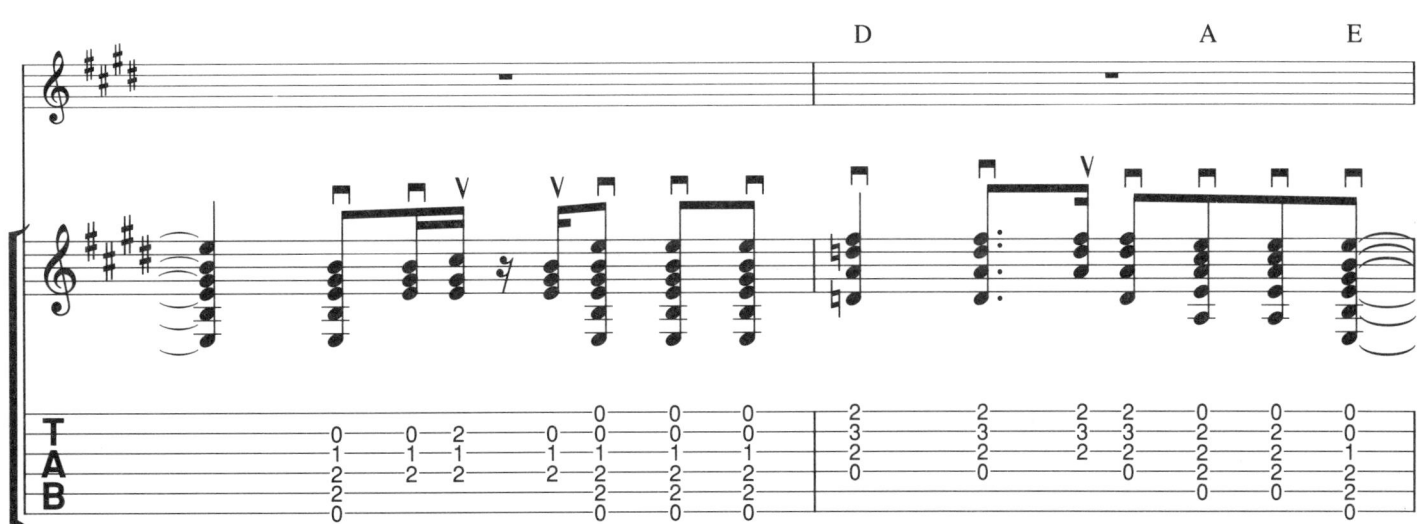

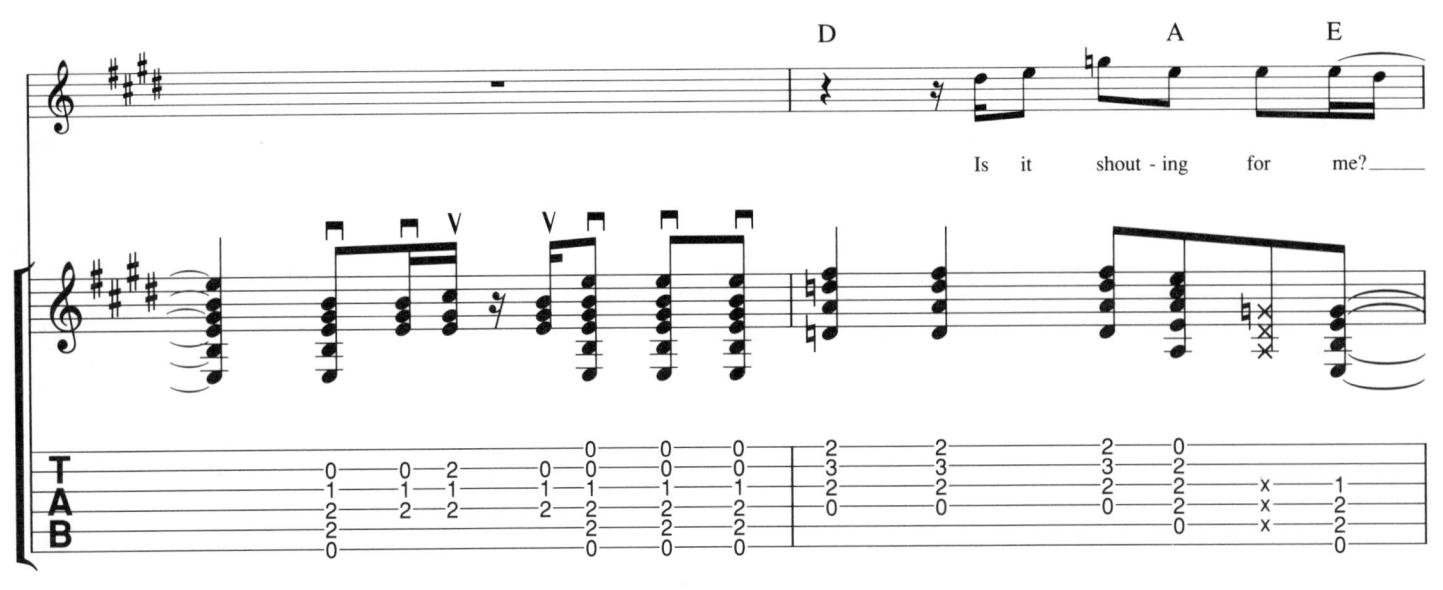

Is it shout-ing for me?_____

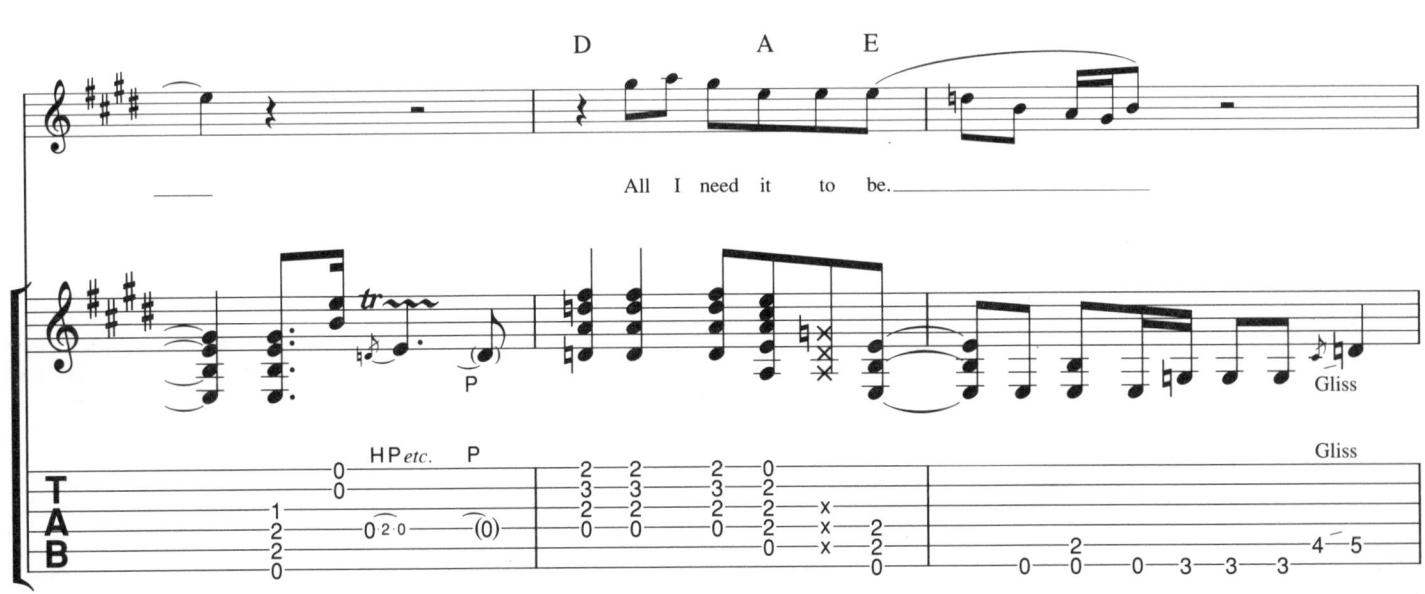

All I need it to be._____

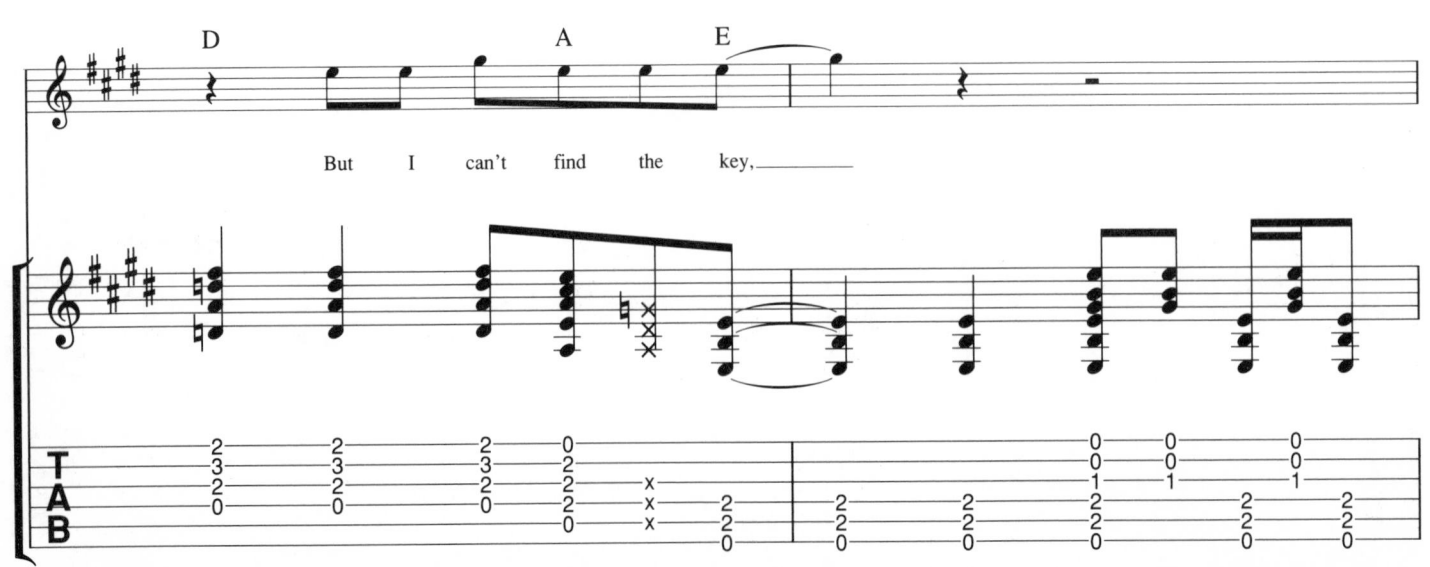

But I can't find the key,_____

46

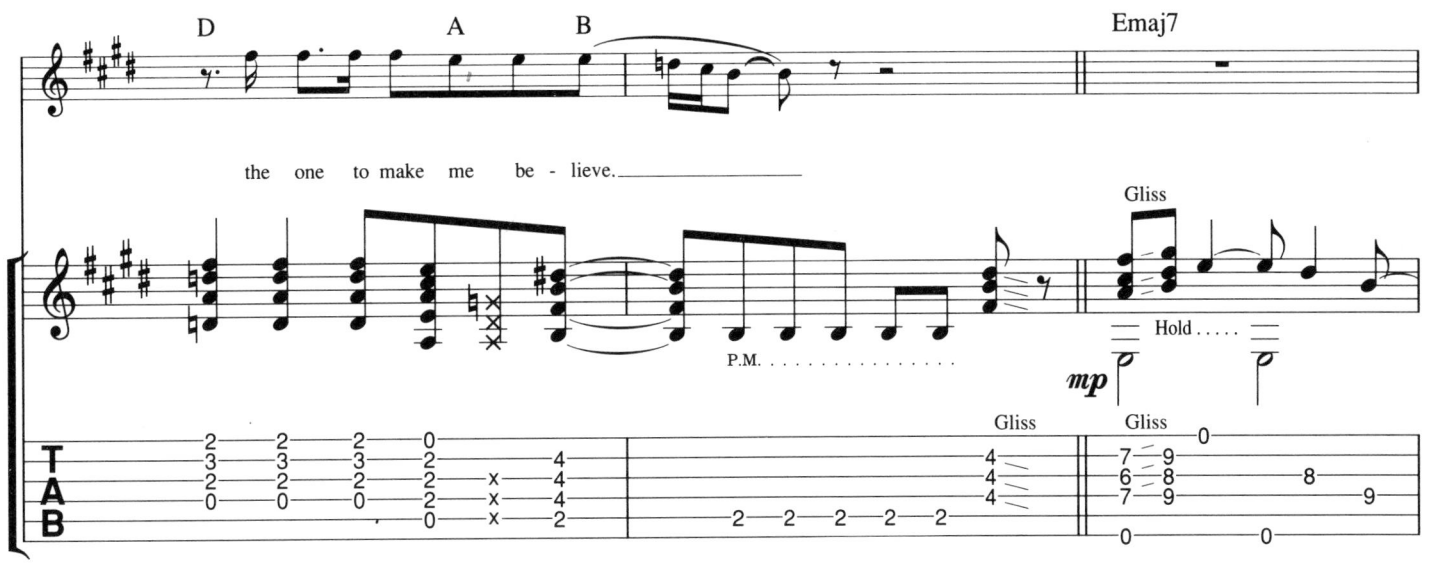

the one to make me be - lieve._____

Solo:

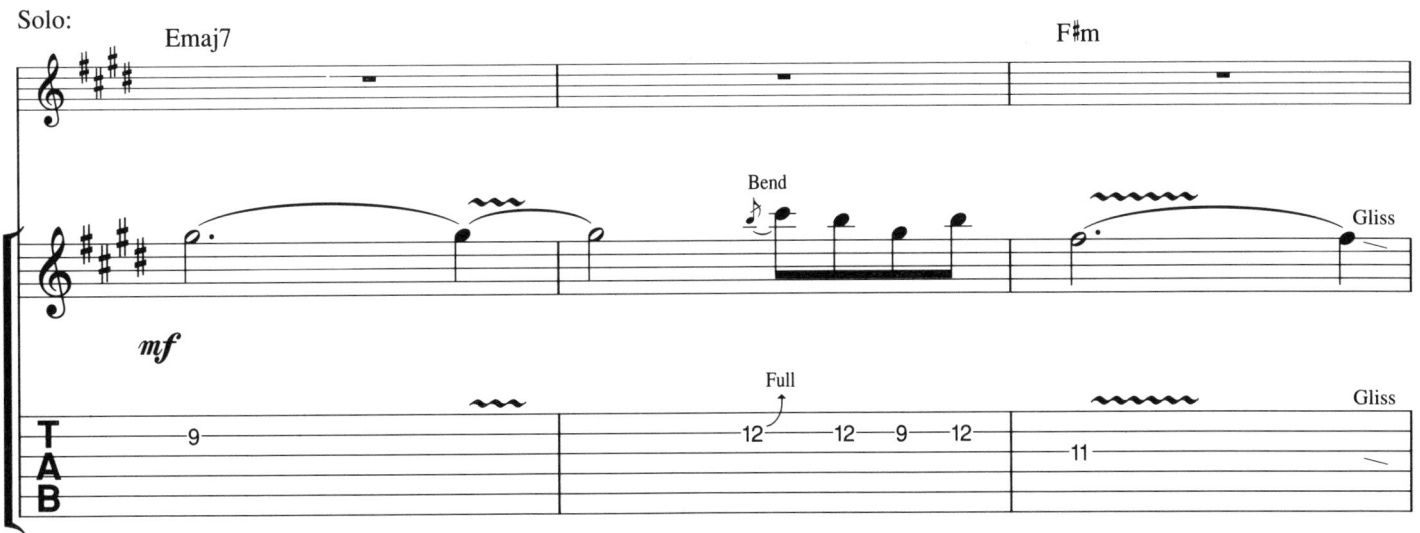

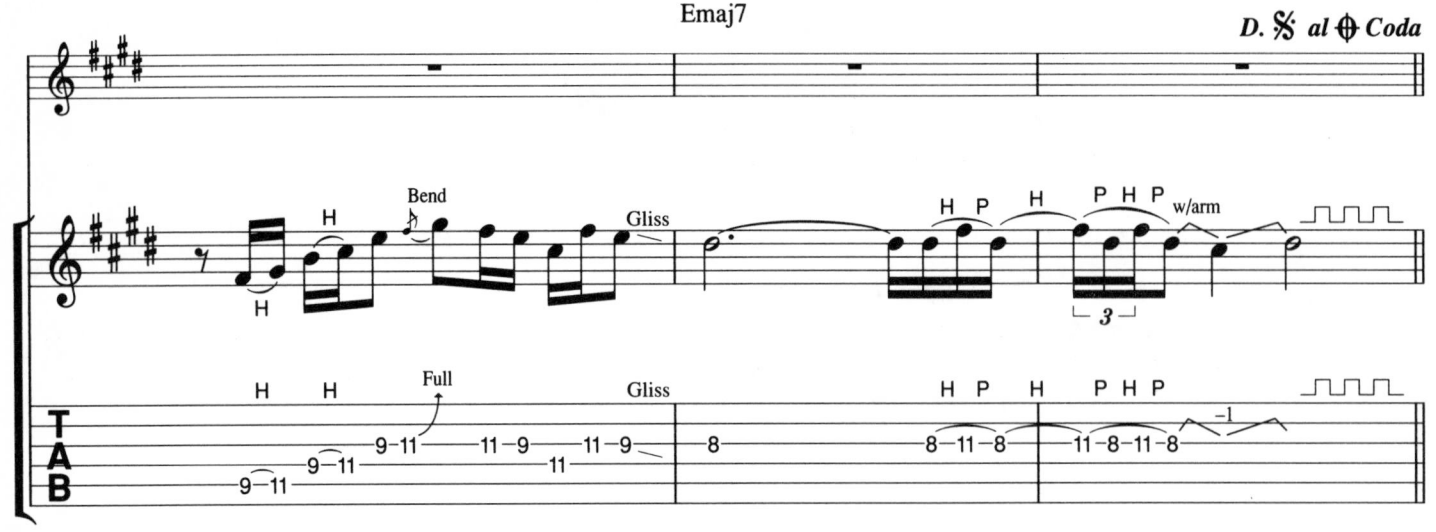

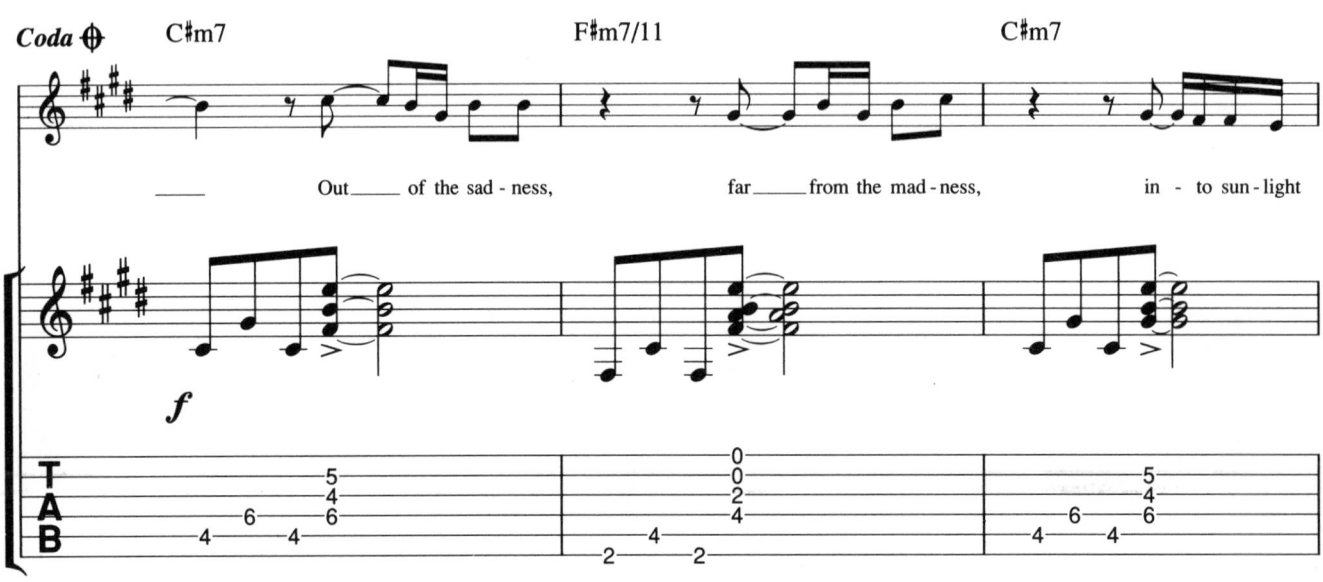

Out___ of the sad - ness,   far___ from the mad - ness,   in - to sun - light

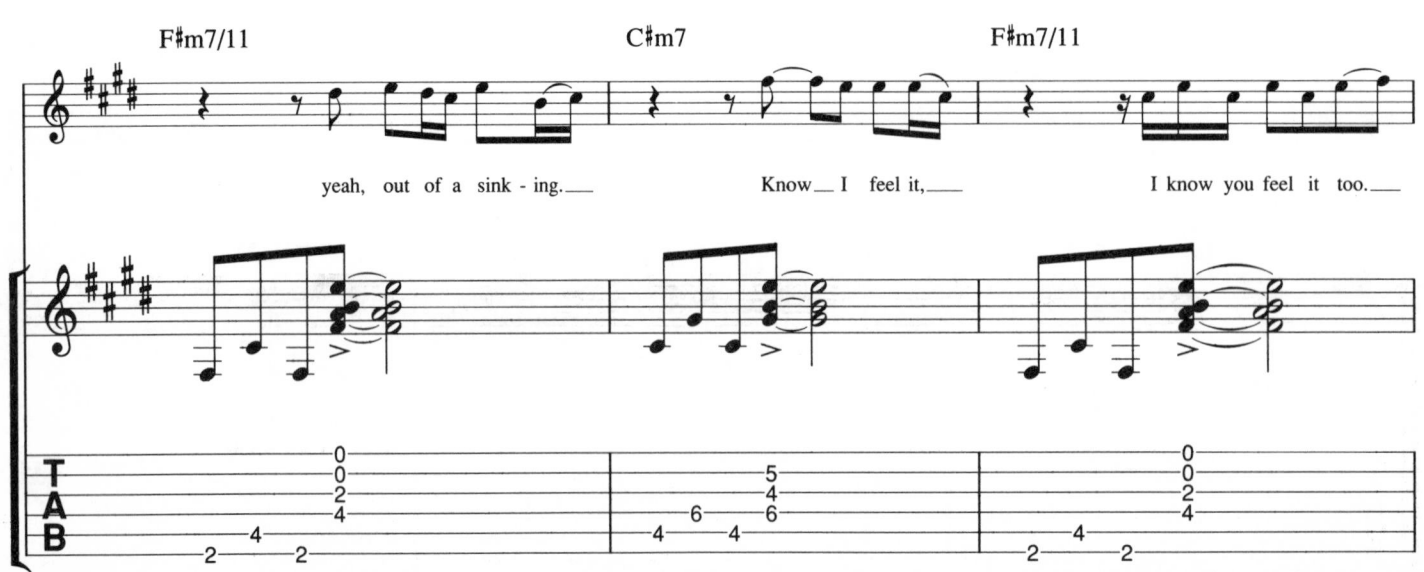

yeah, out of a sink - ing.___   Know__ I feel it,___   I know you feel it too.___

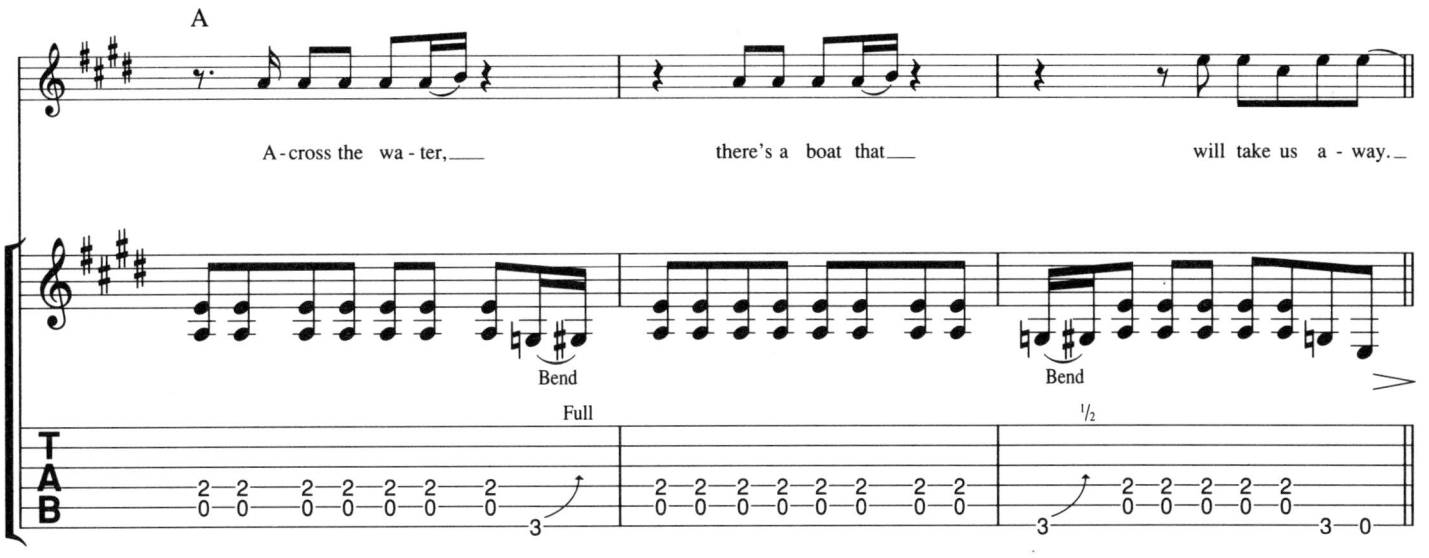

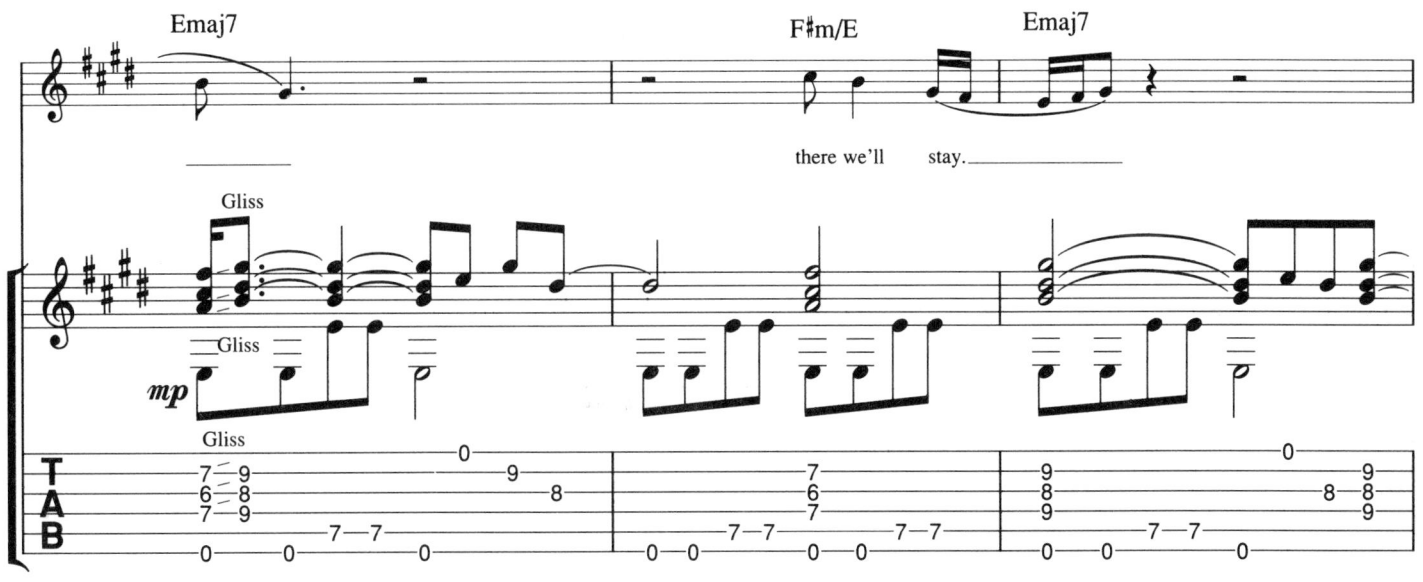

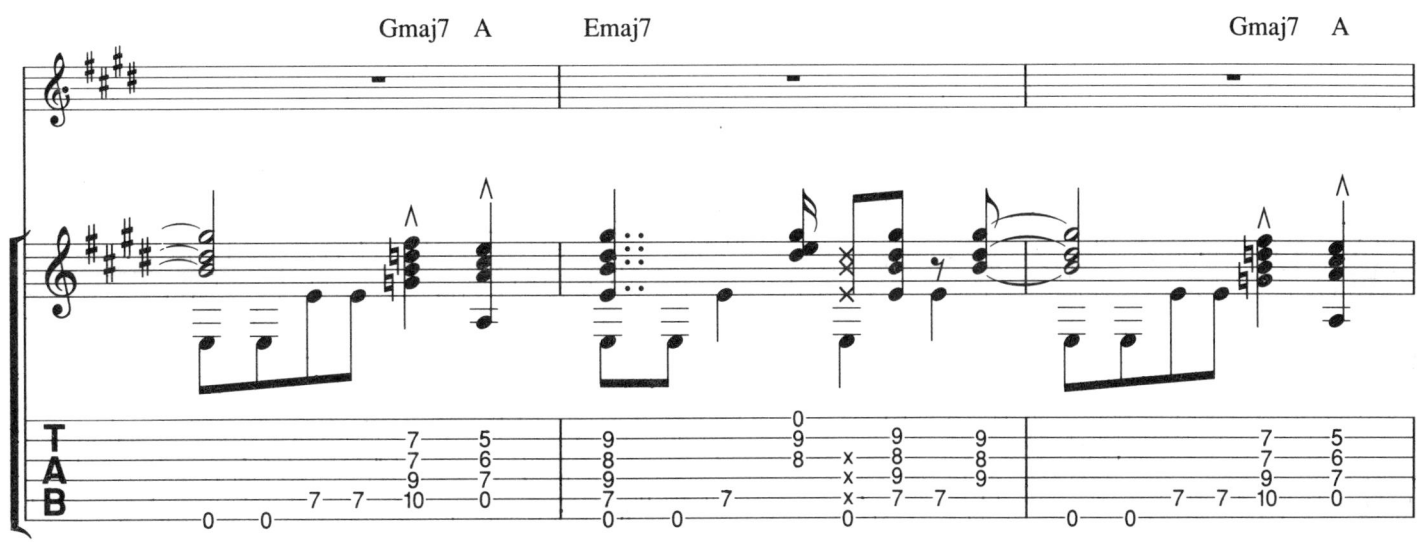

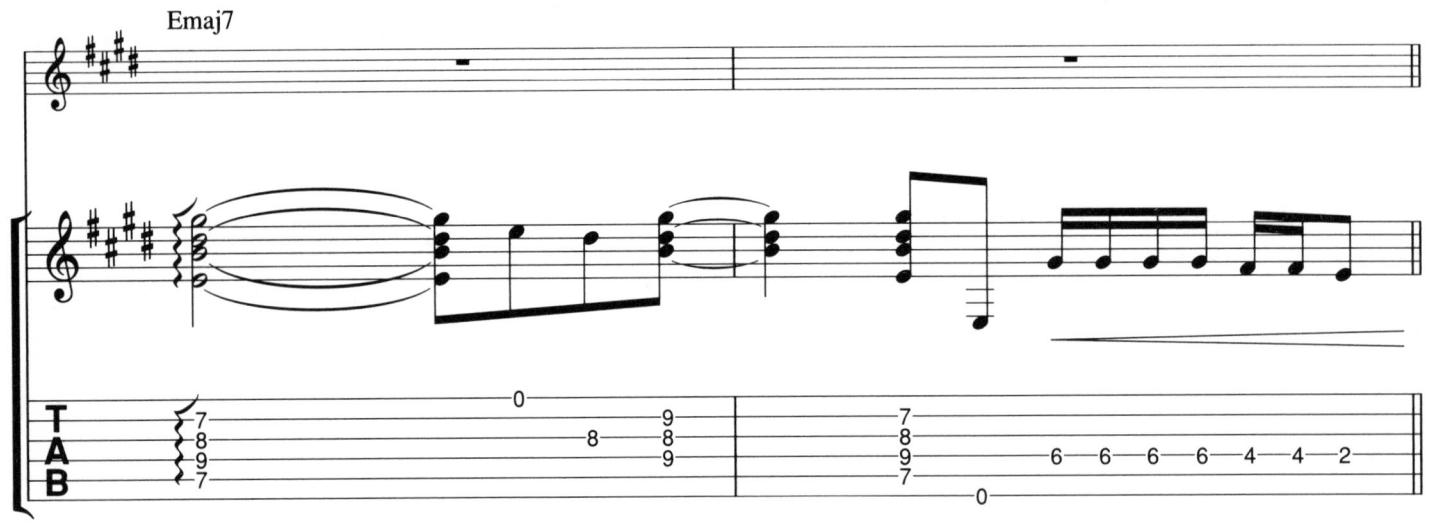

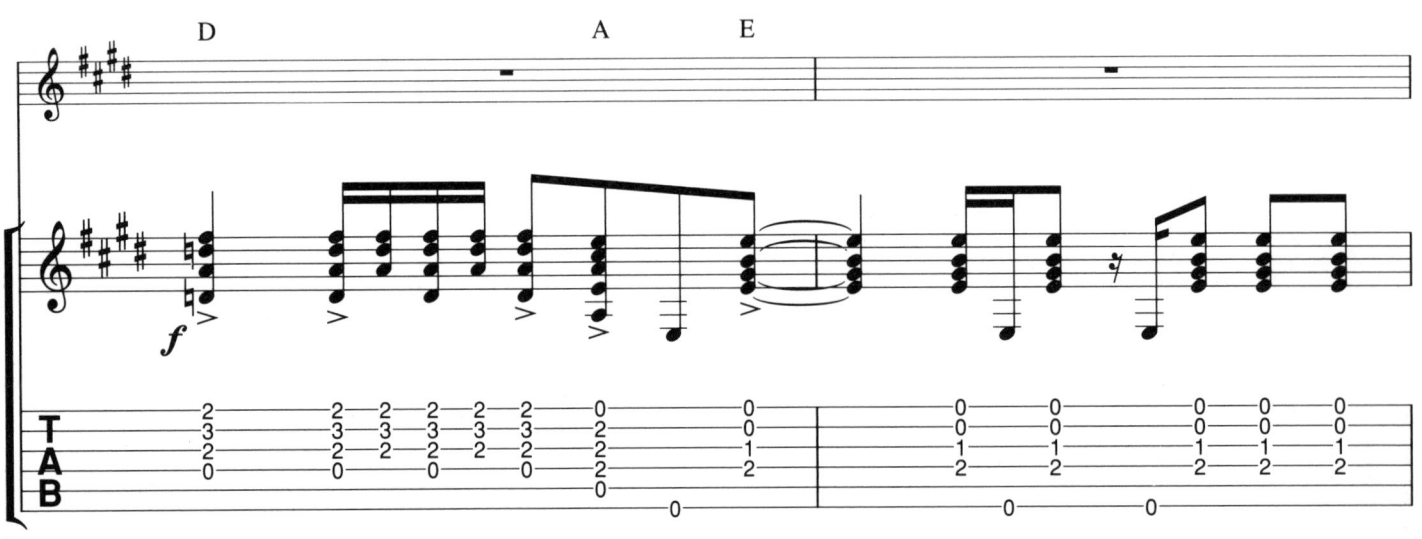

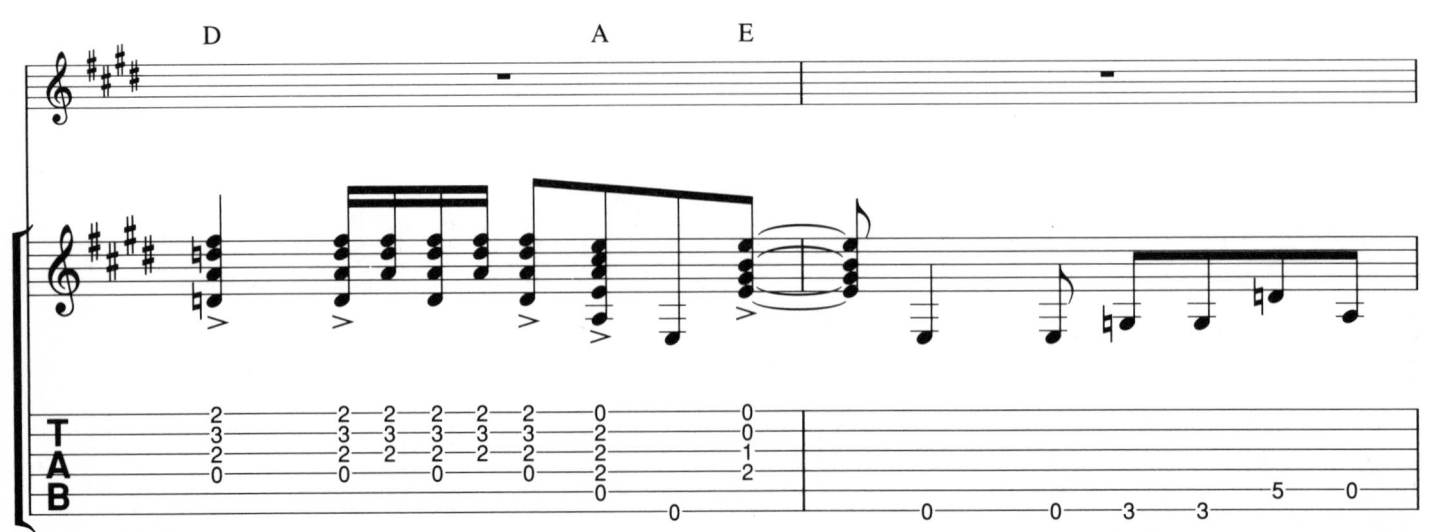

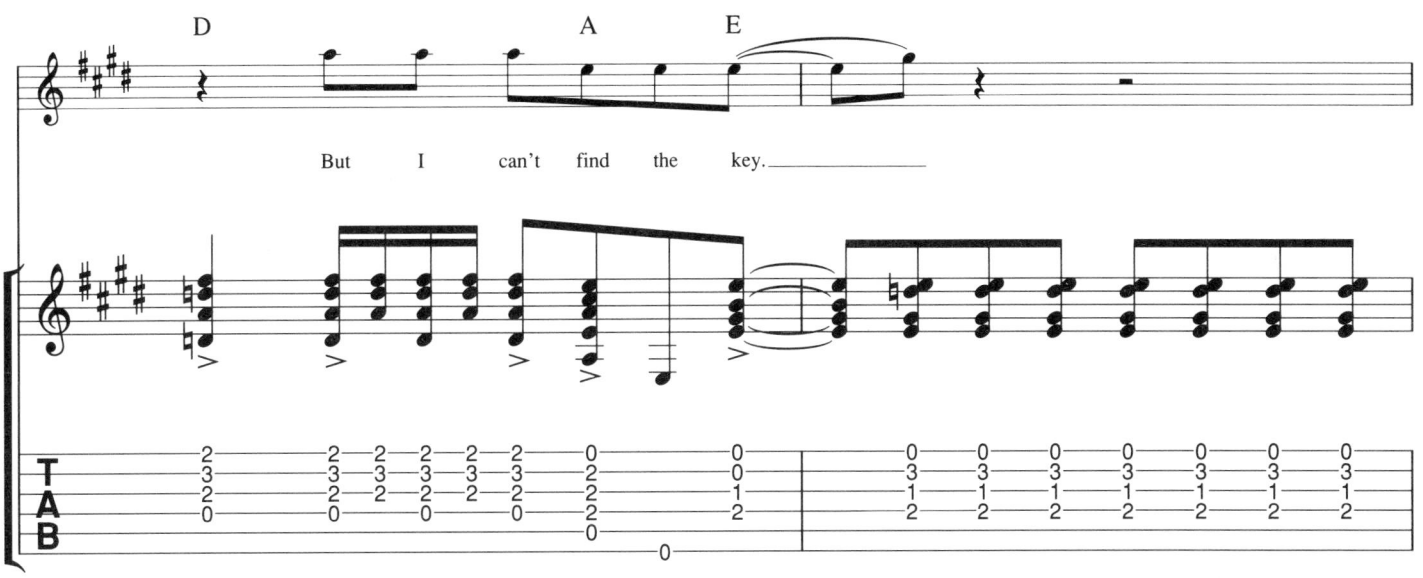

But I can't find the key.

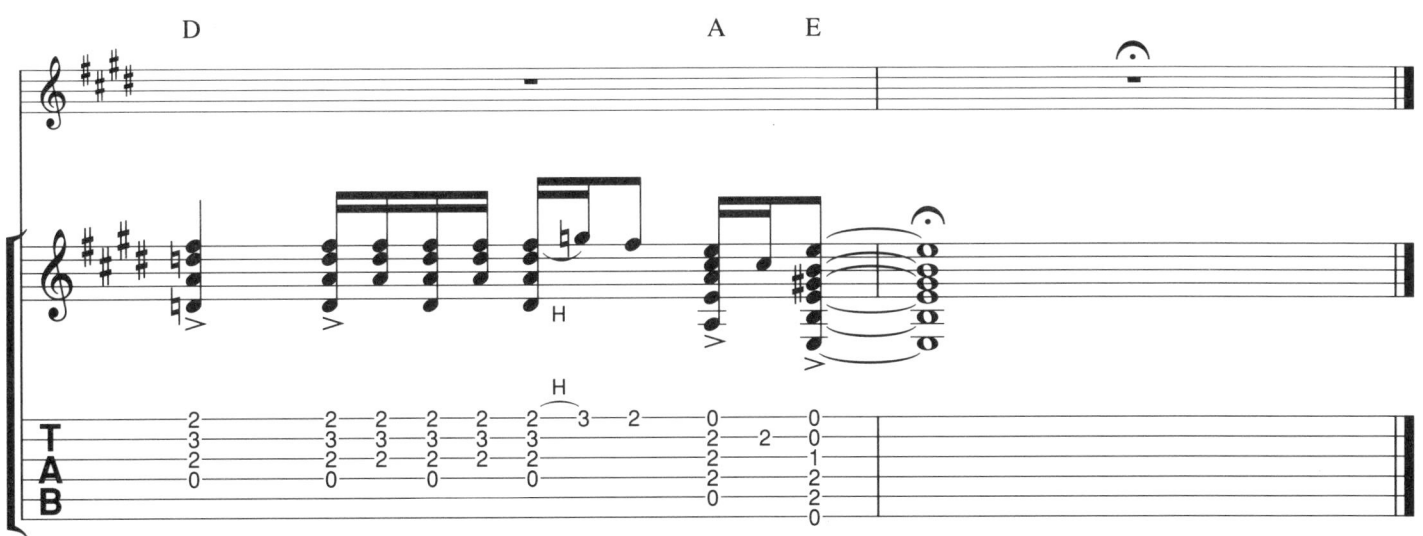

Verse 2(𝄋)
Late at night
When the world is dreaming
Way past the stars
That ignore our fate
And all twinkle too late to save us
So we save ourselves.

Chorus 2:
Hey baby, do just what you're thinking
Know I know it, yeah, feel I'm sinking
Konw I feel it, I know you feel it too
Across the water is a boat that will take us away.

stanley road

words & music by paul weller

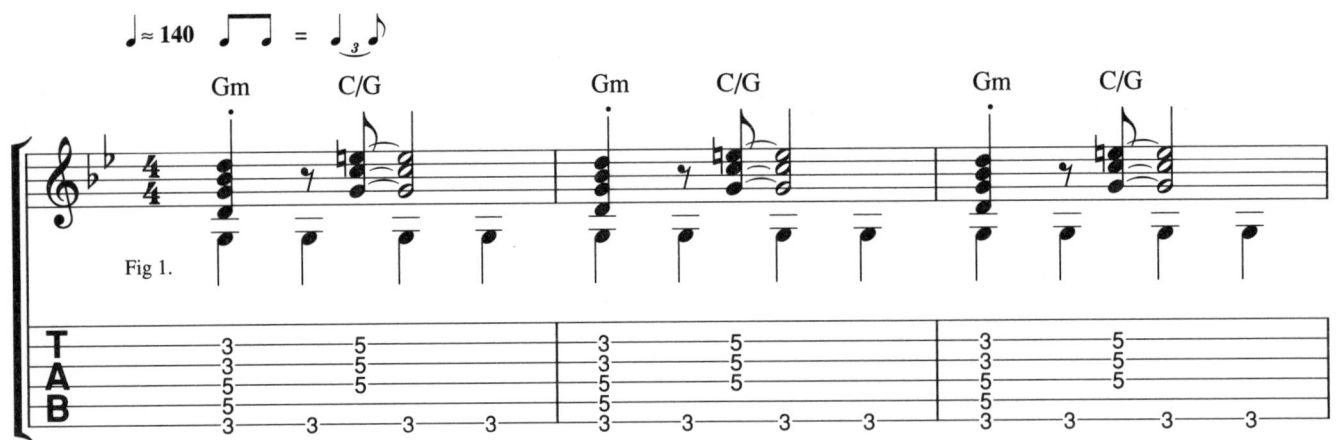

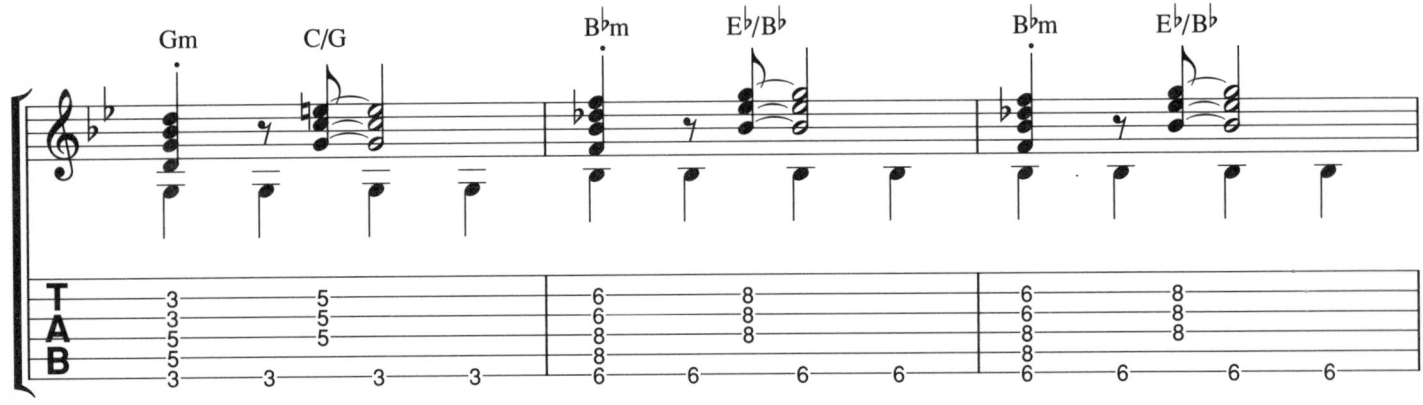

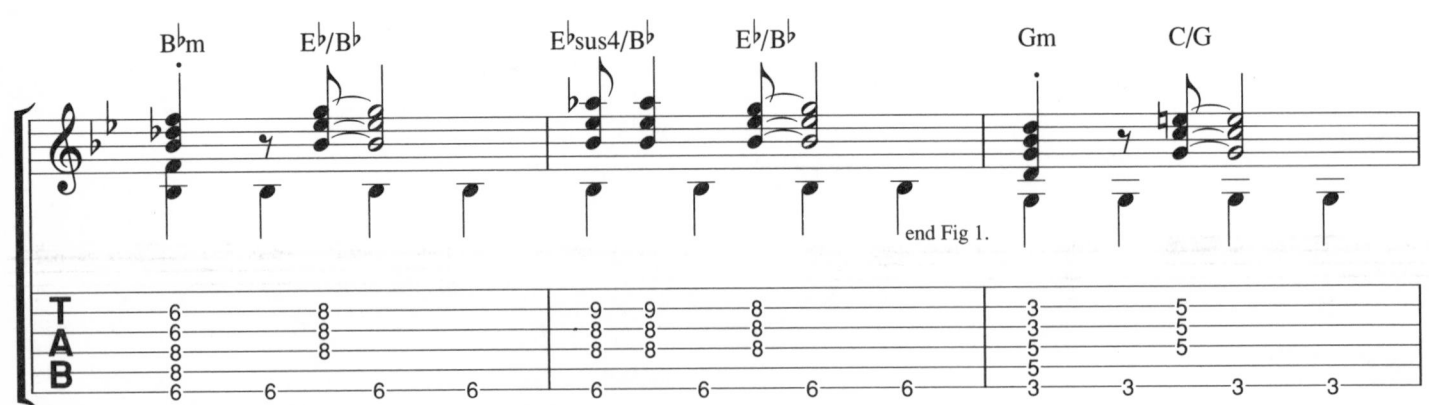

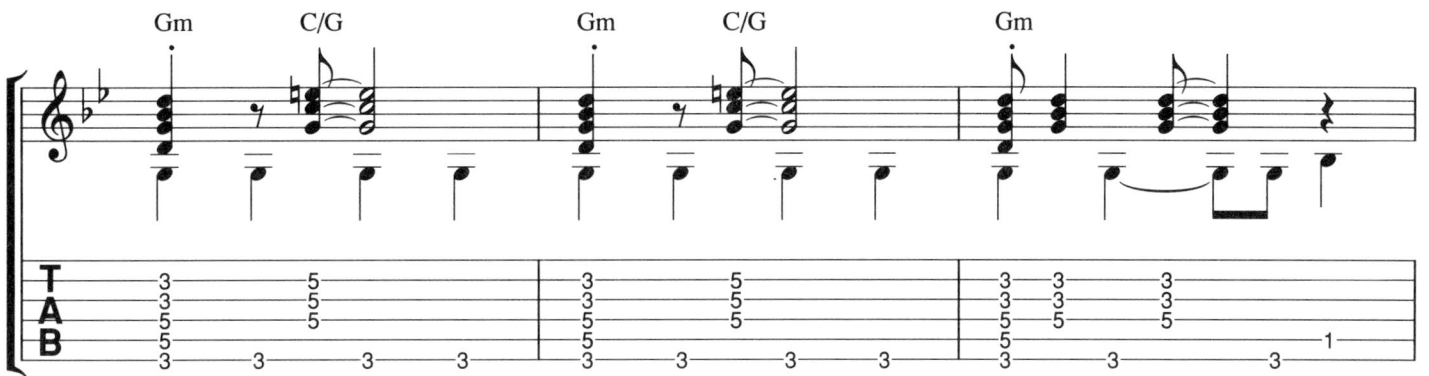

Verse:

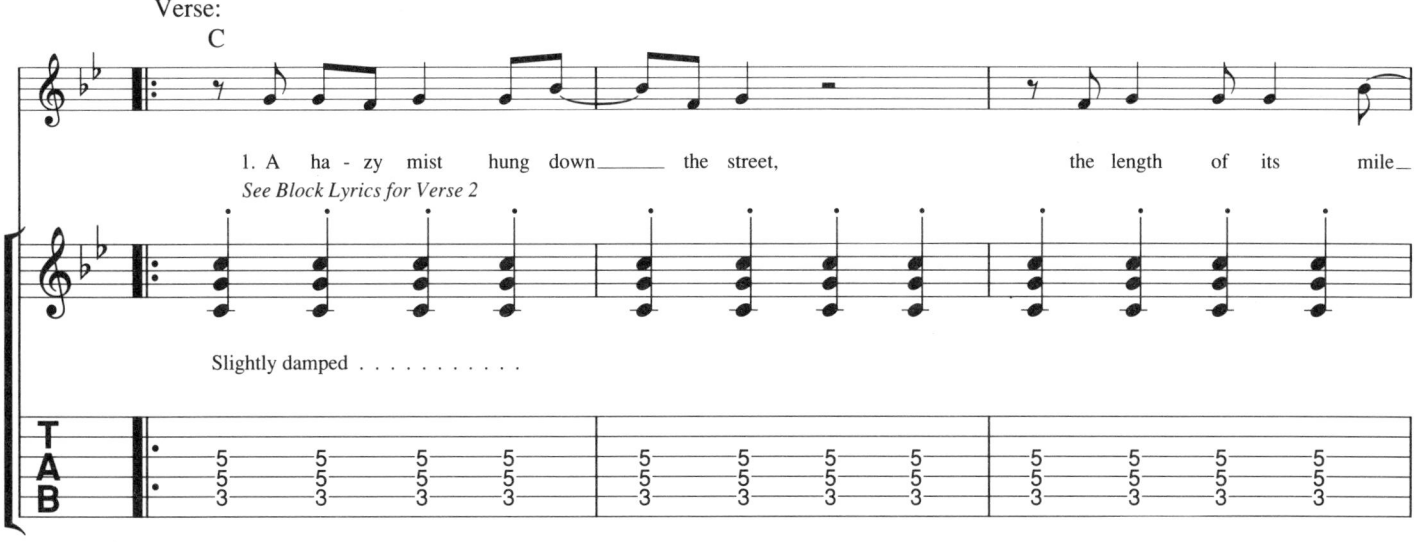

1. A ha - zy mist hung down_____ the street, the length of its mile__
See Block Lyrics for Verse 2

Slightly damped . . . .

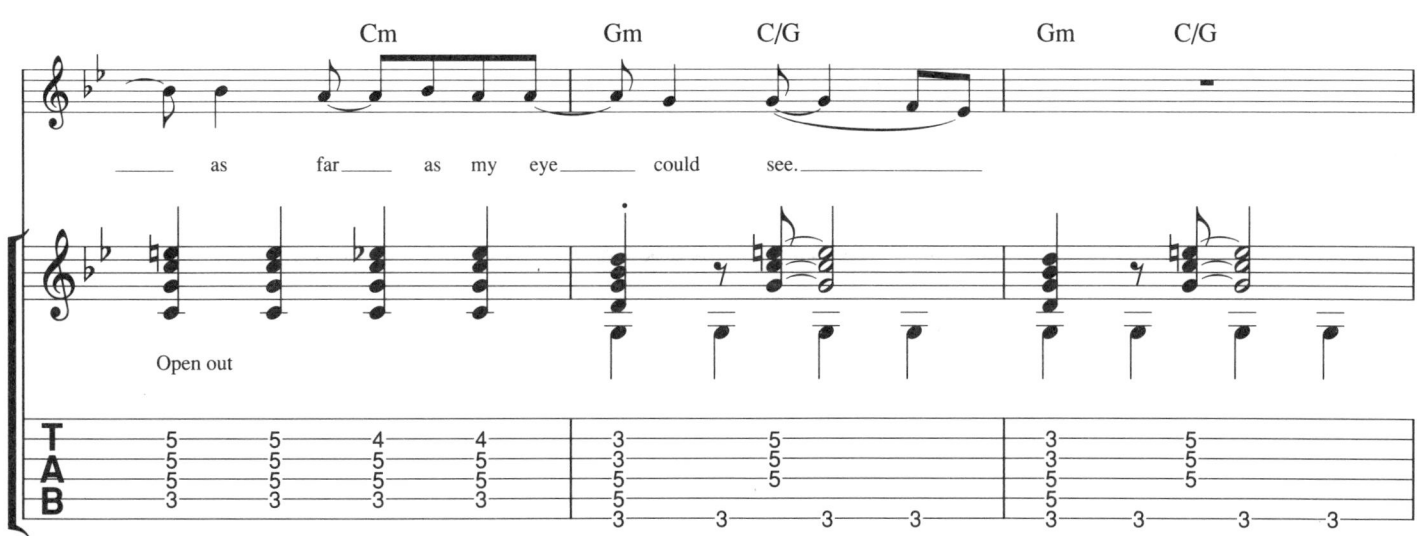

____ as far___ as my eye___ could see._____

Open out

The sky so wide, the hou-

Slightly damped

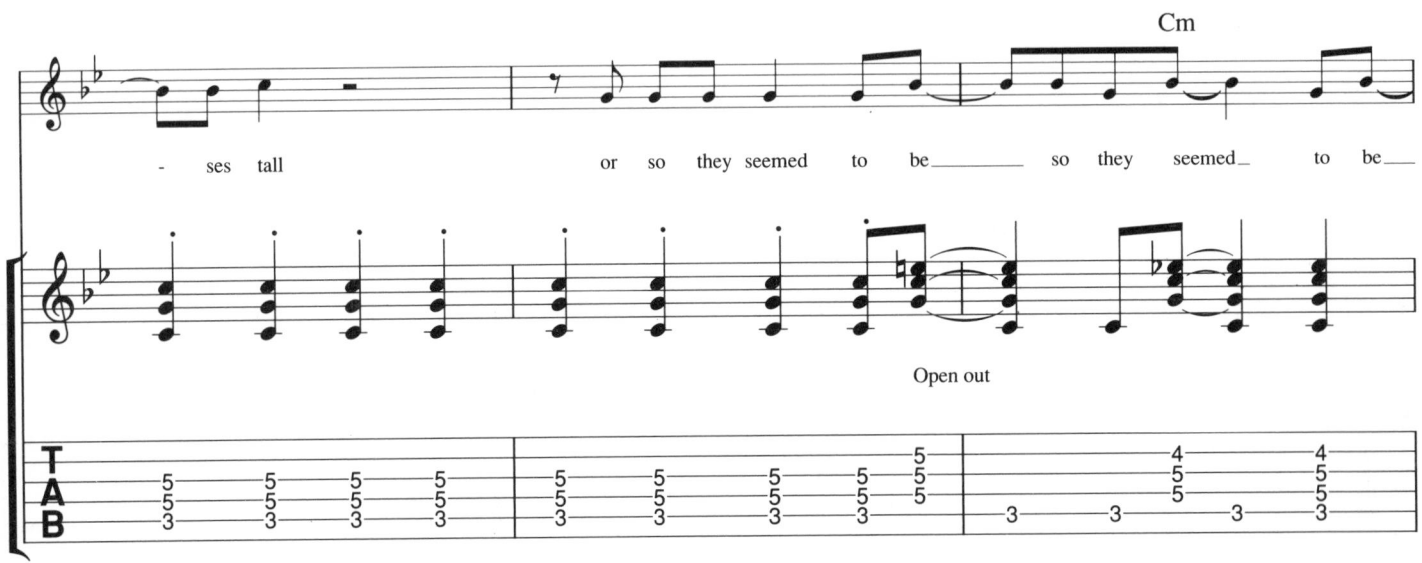

- ses tall   or so they seemed to be_____ so they seemed___ to be_____

Open out

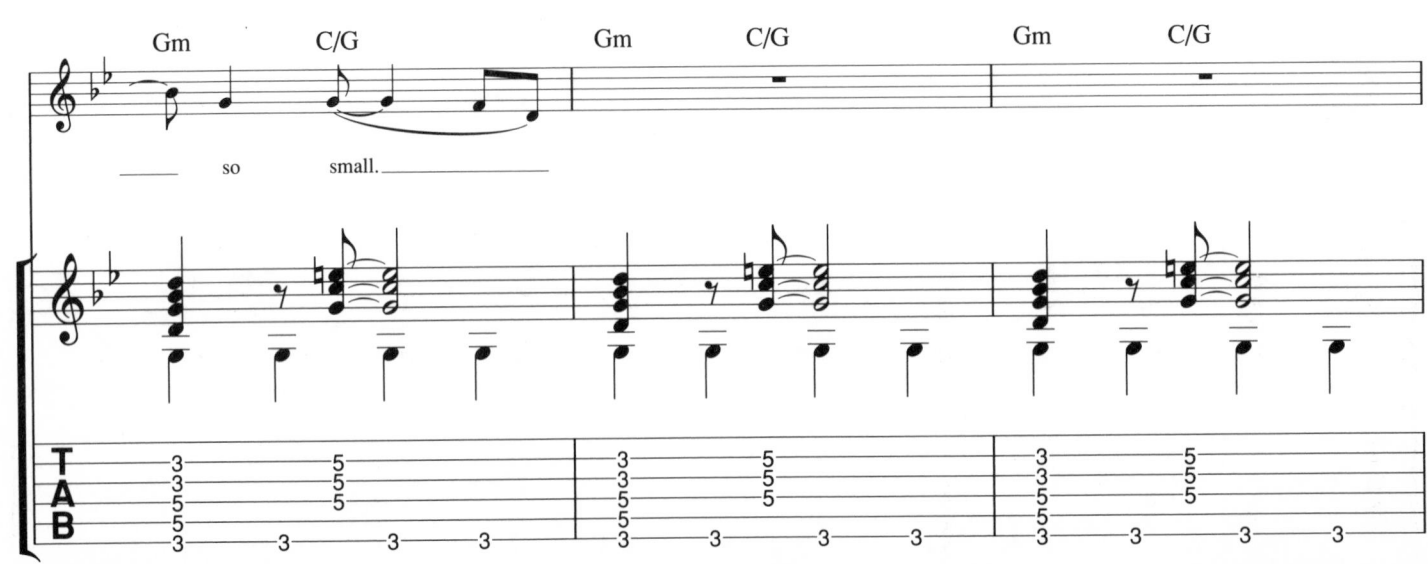

_____ so   small._____

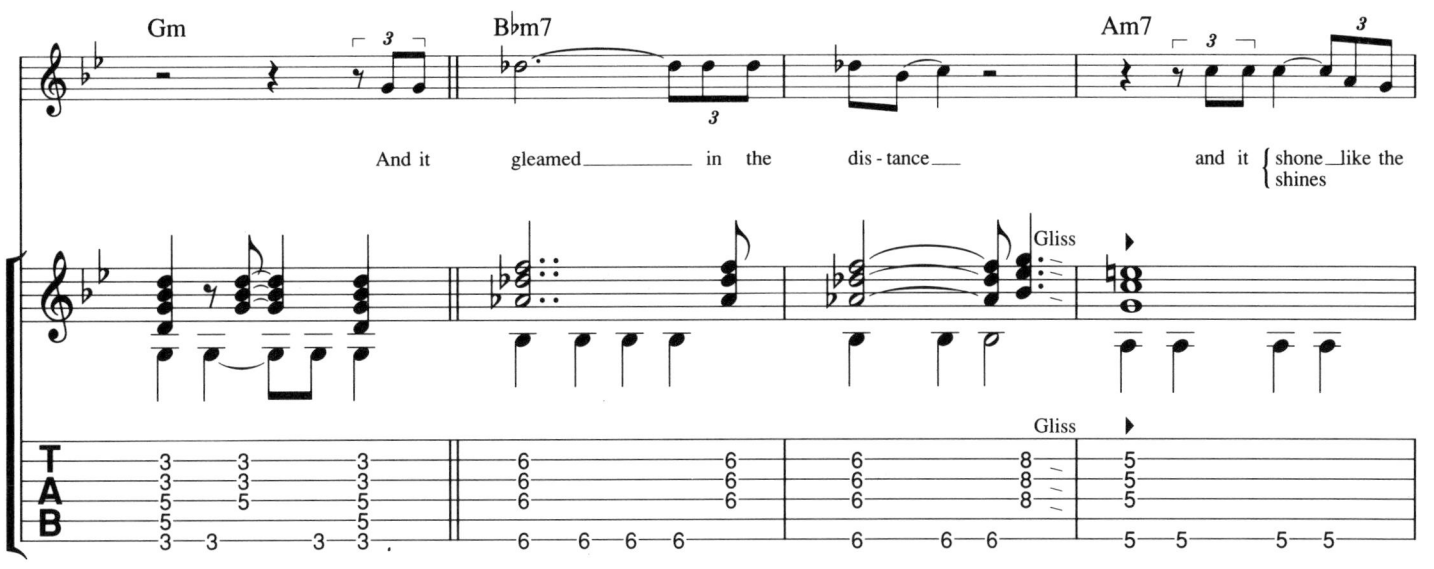

And it gleamed_____ in the dis-tance_____ and it { shone_like the / shines

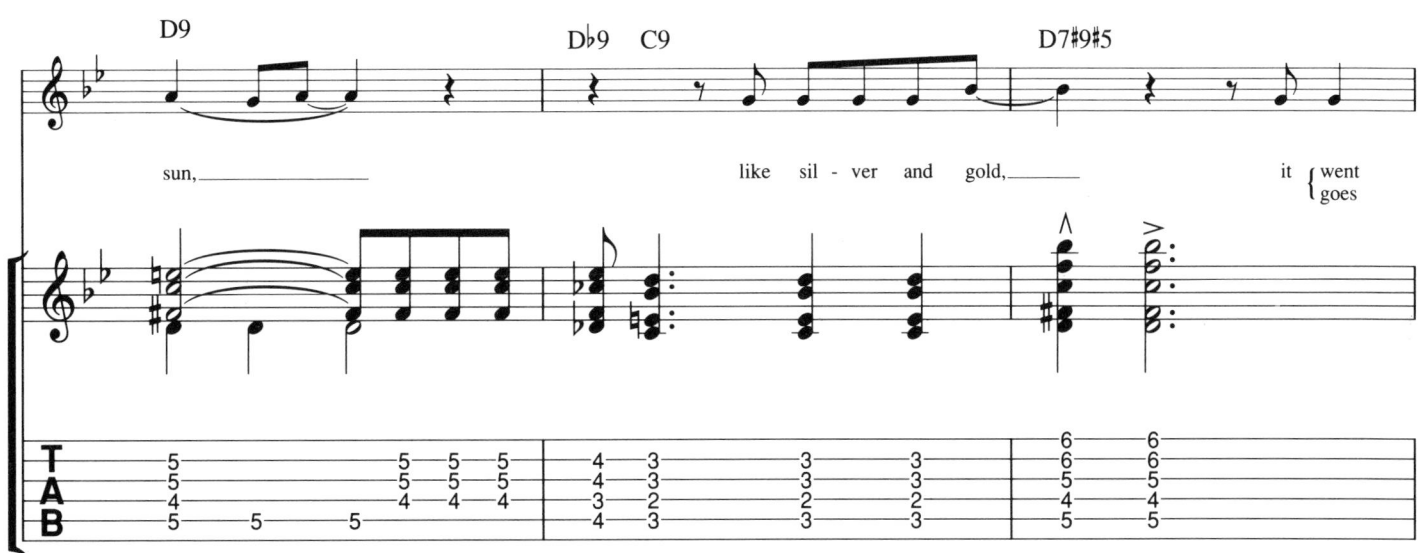

sun,_____ like sil - ver and gold,_____ it { went / goes

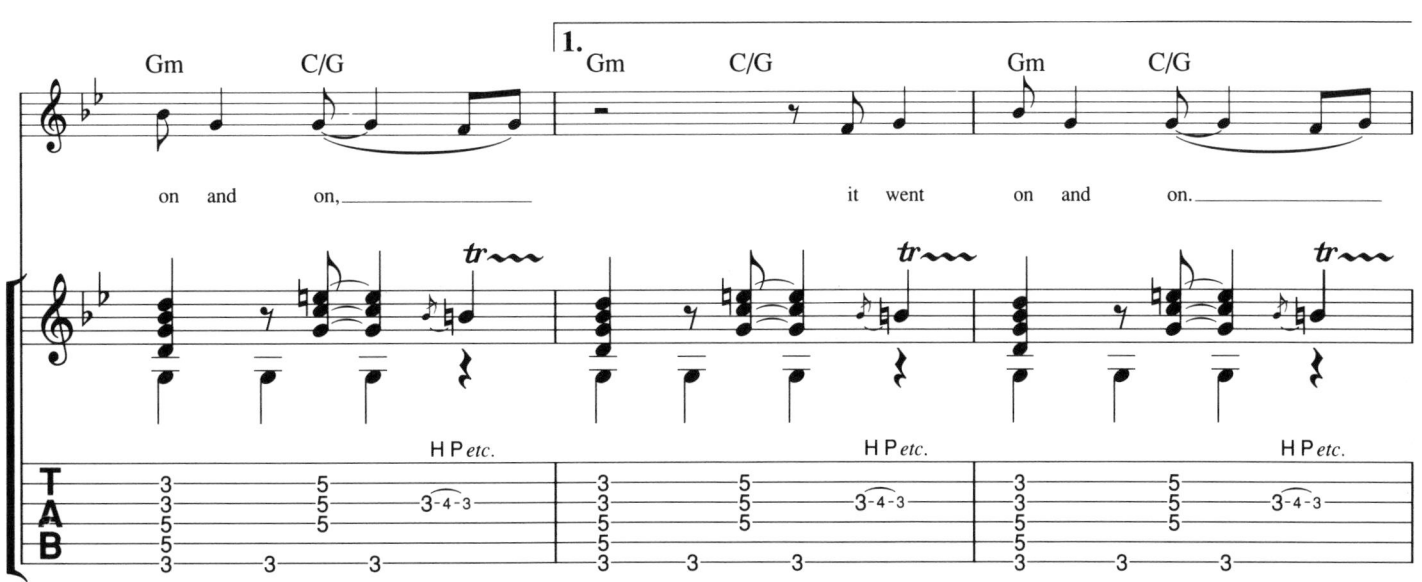

on and on,_____ it went on and on._____

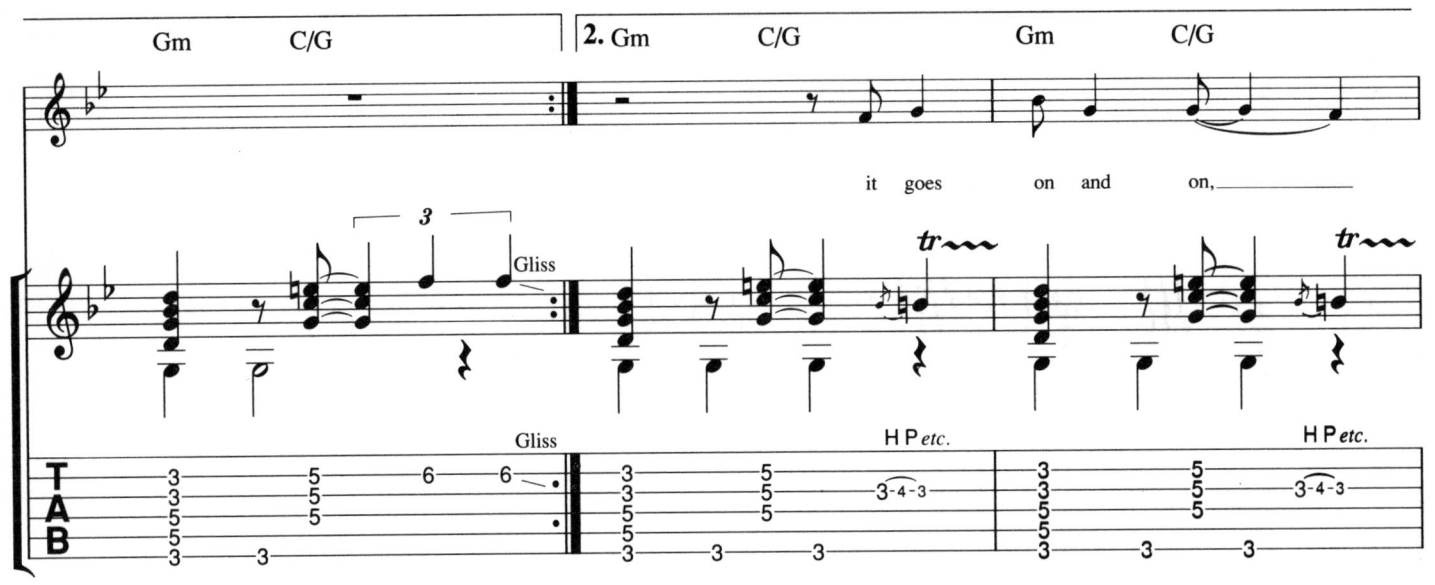

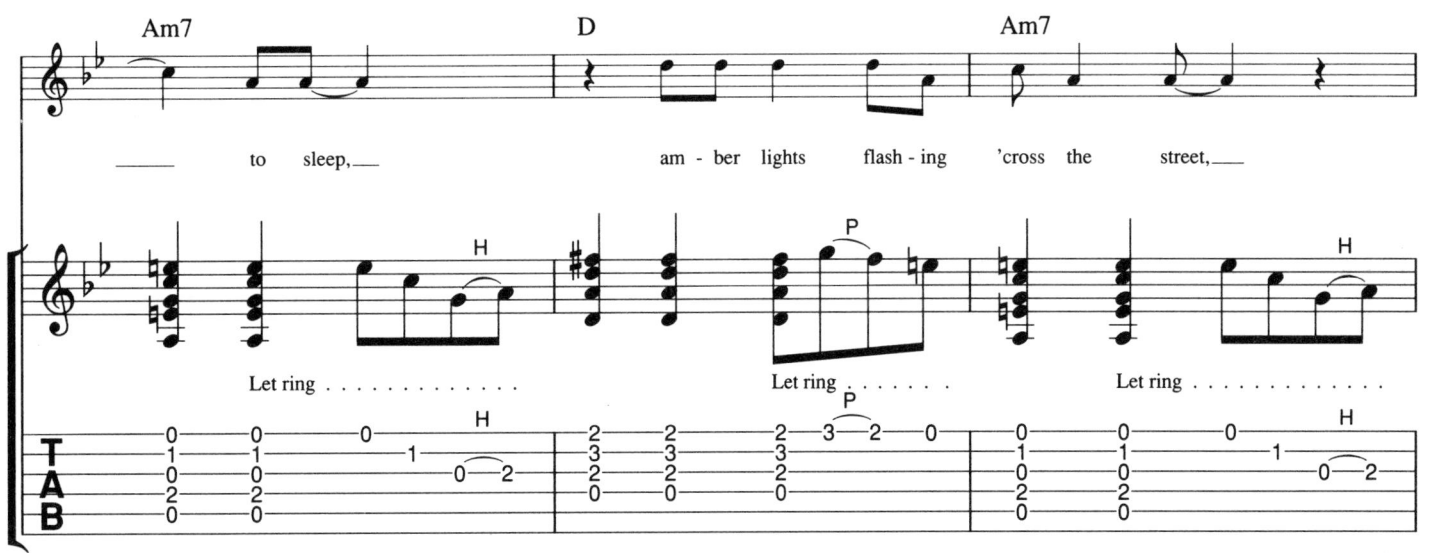

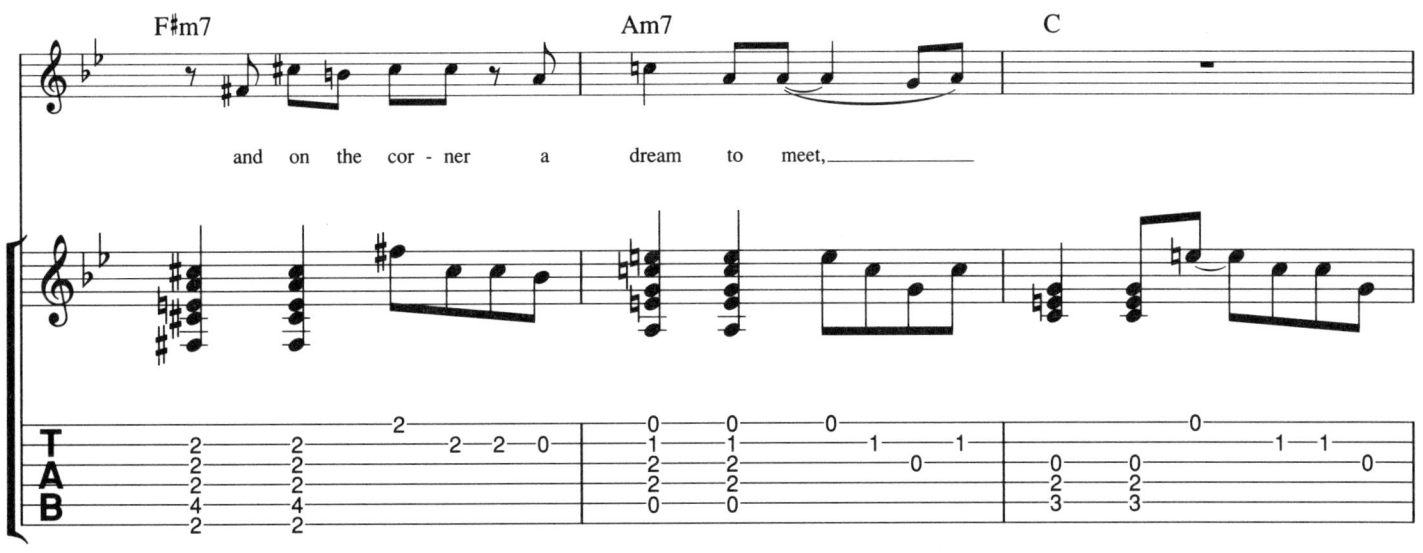

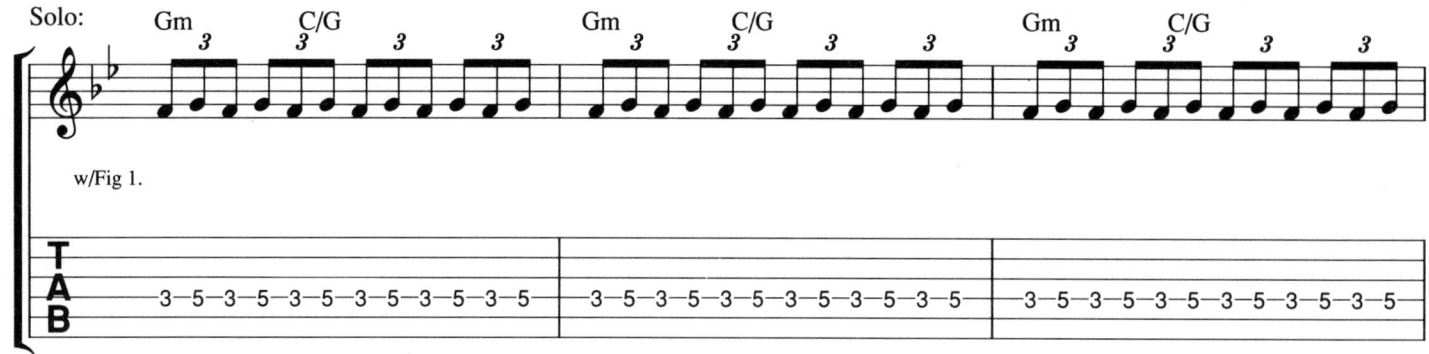

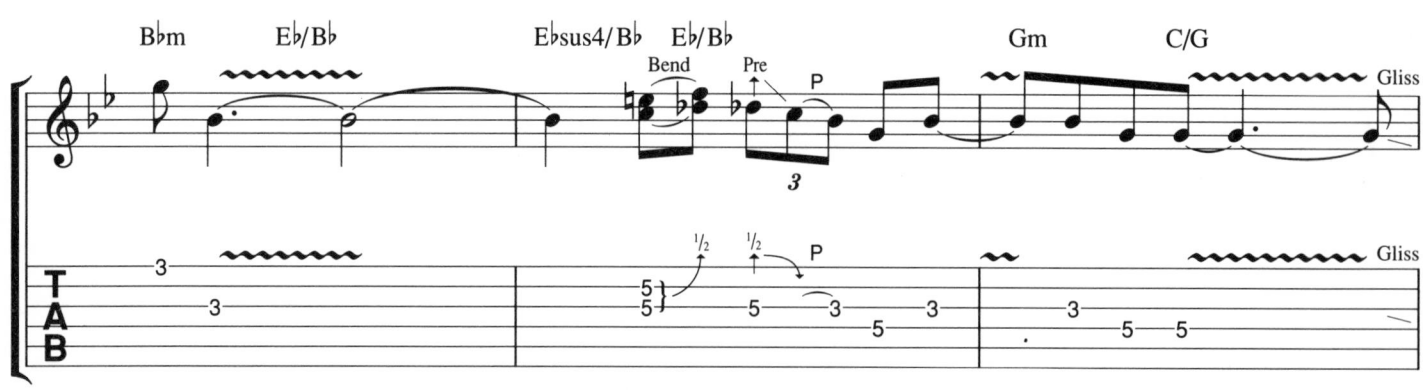

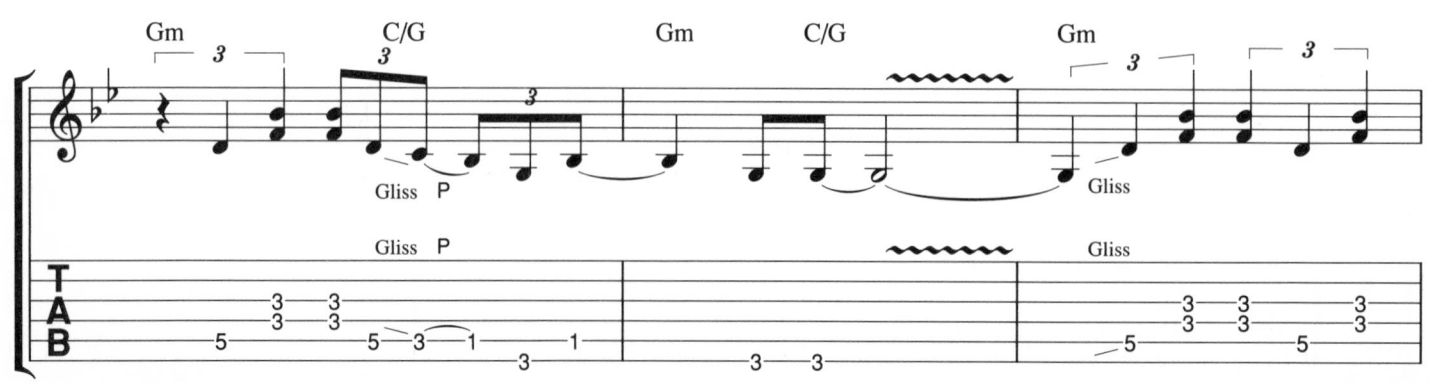

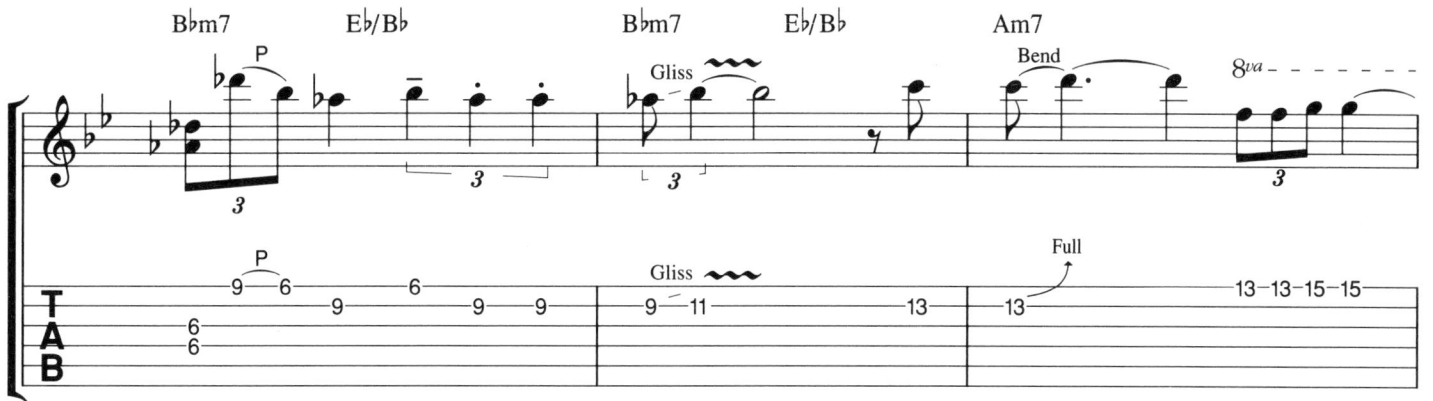

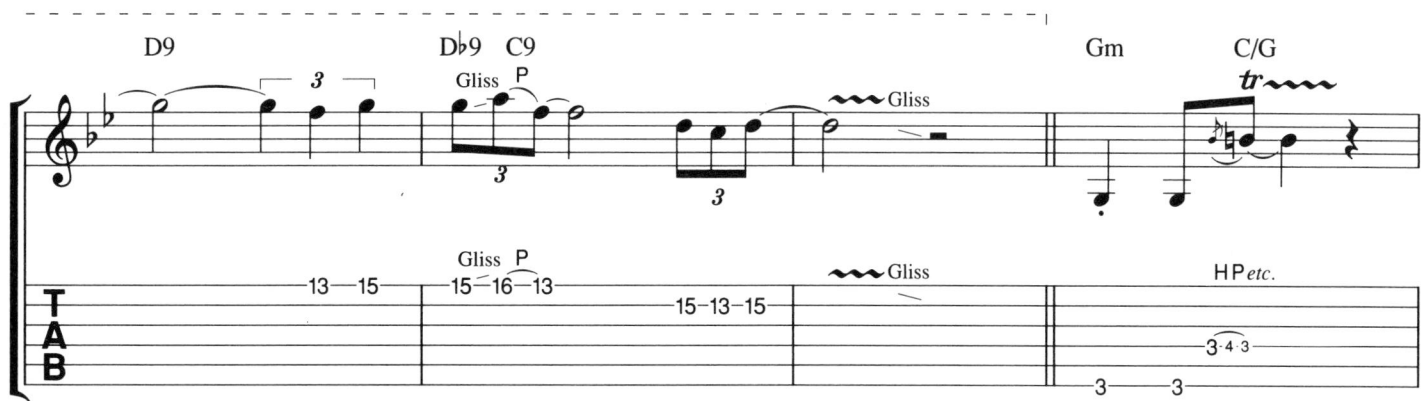

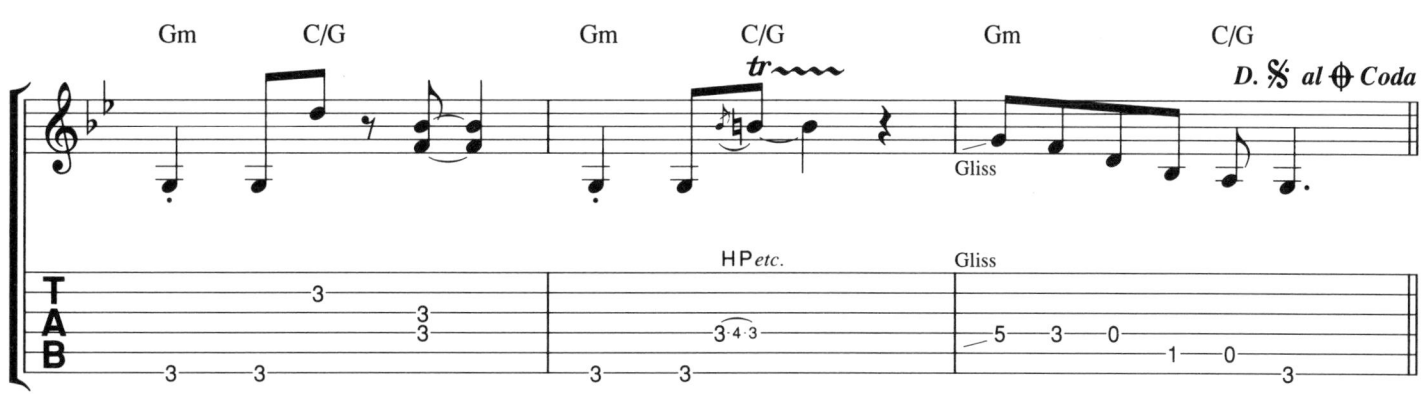

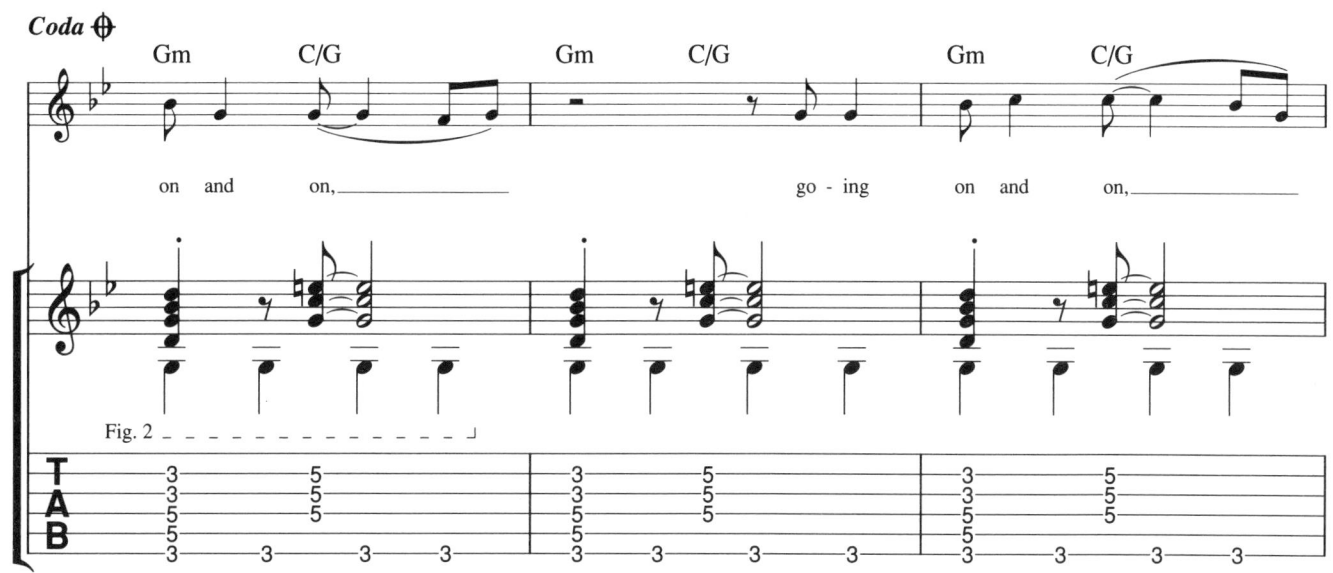

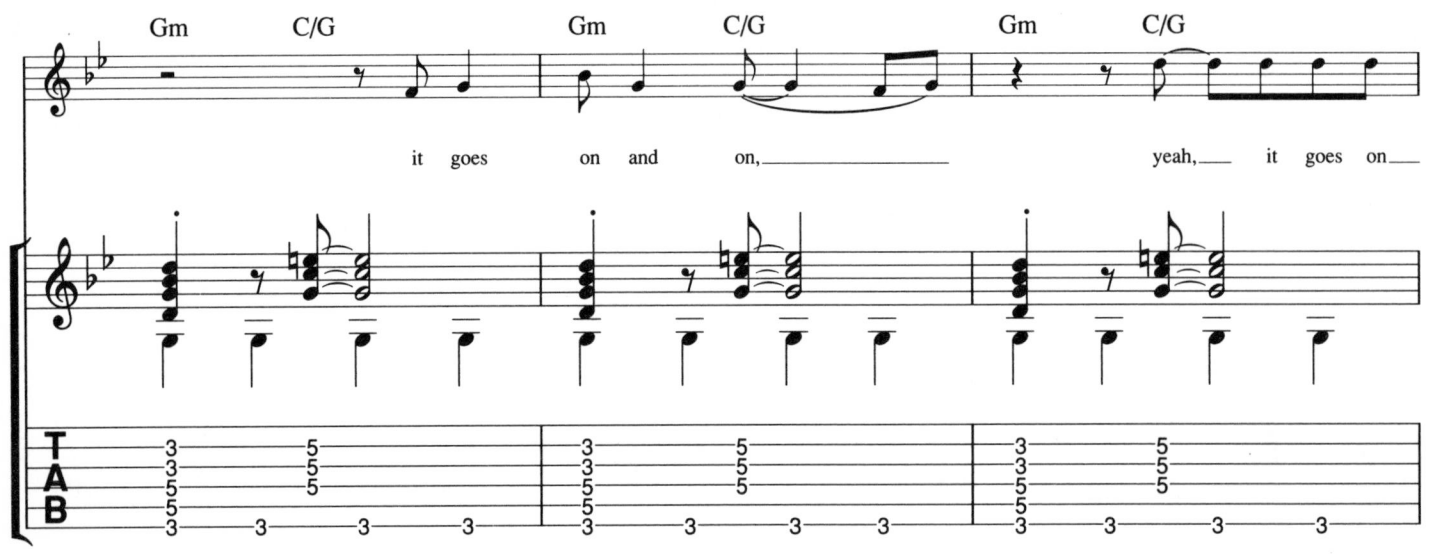

it goes on and on,_____ yeah,___ it goes on

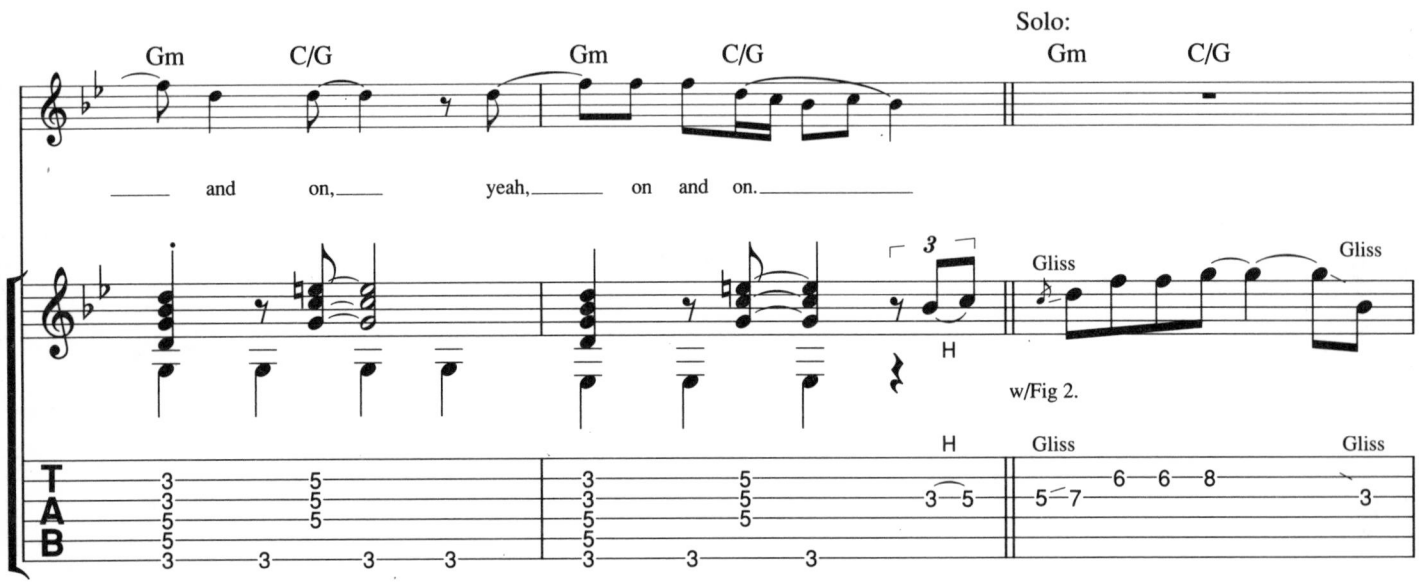

____ and on,___ yeah,_____ on and on._____

Solo:

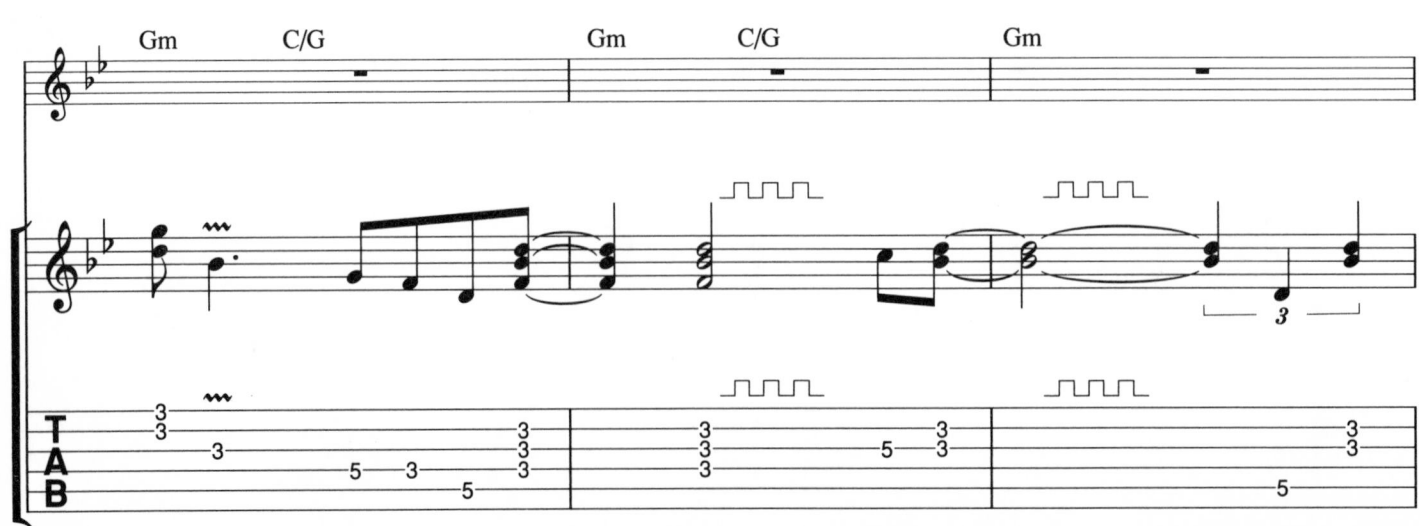

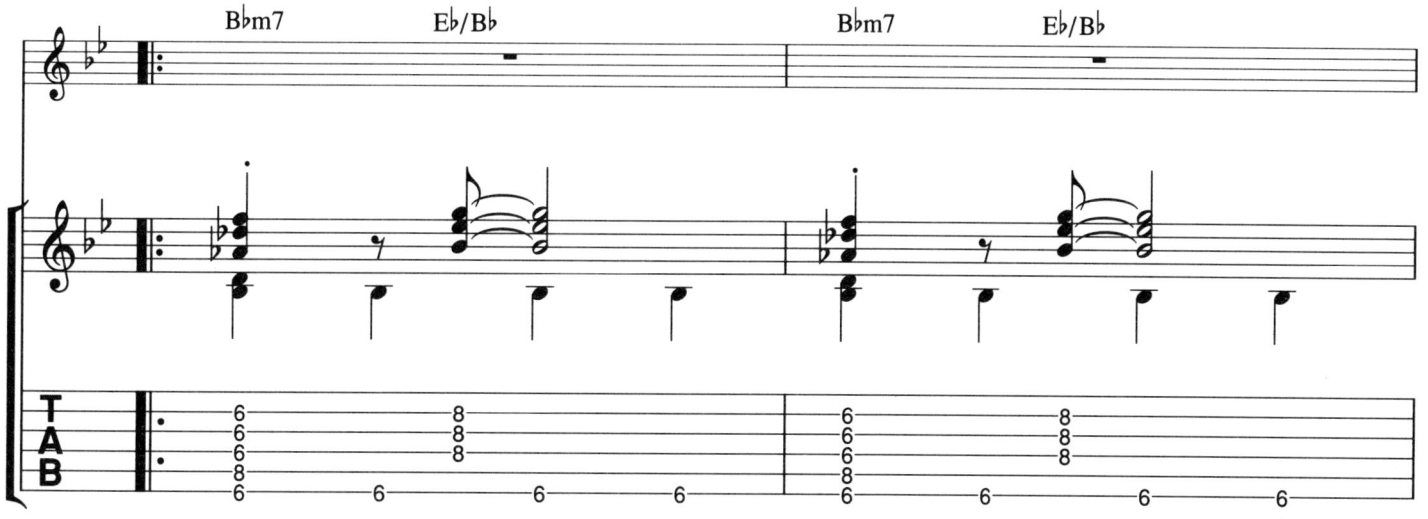

Repeat with ad lib solo to fade

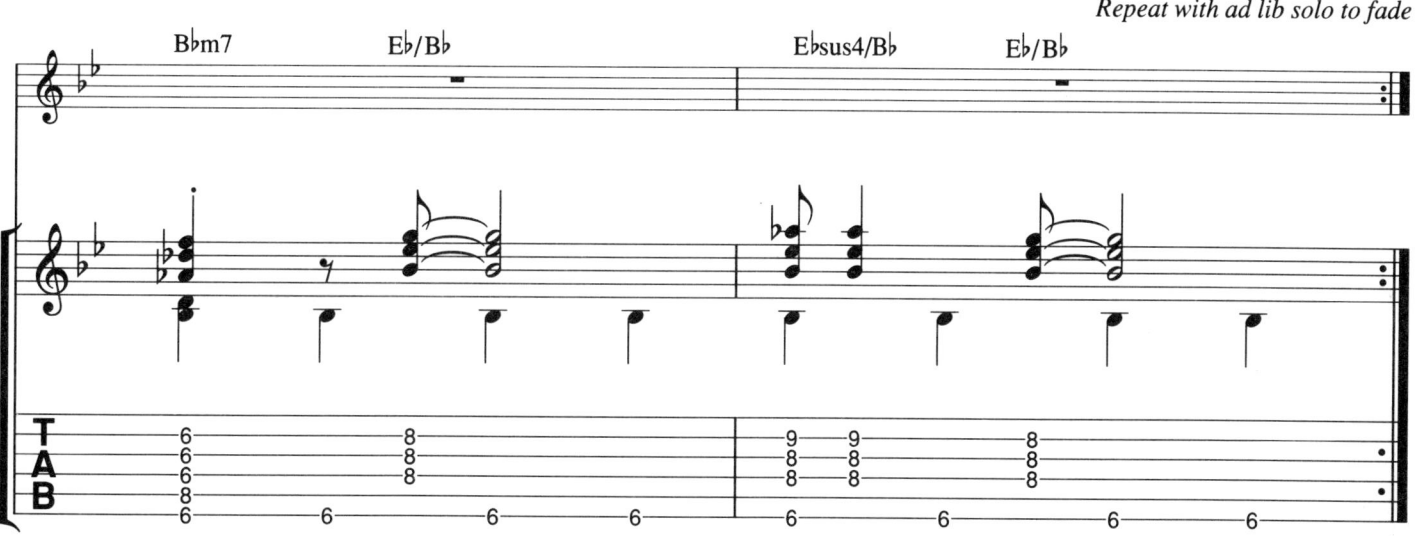

Verse 2:
The summer nights that seemed so long
Always call me back to return
As I rewrite this song.
The ghosts of night, the dreams of day
Make me swirl and fall and hold me
In their sway.

sunflower

words & music by paul weller

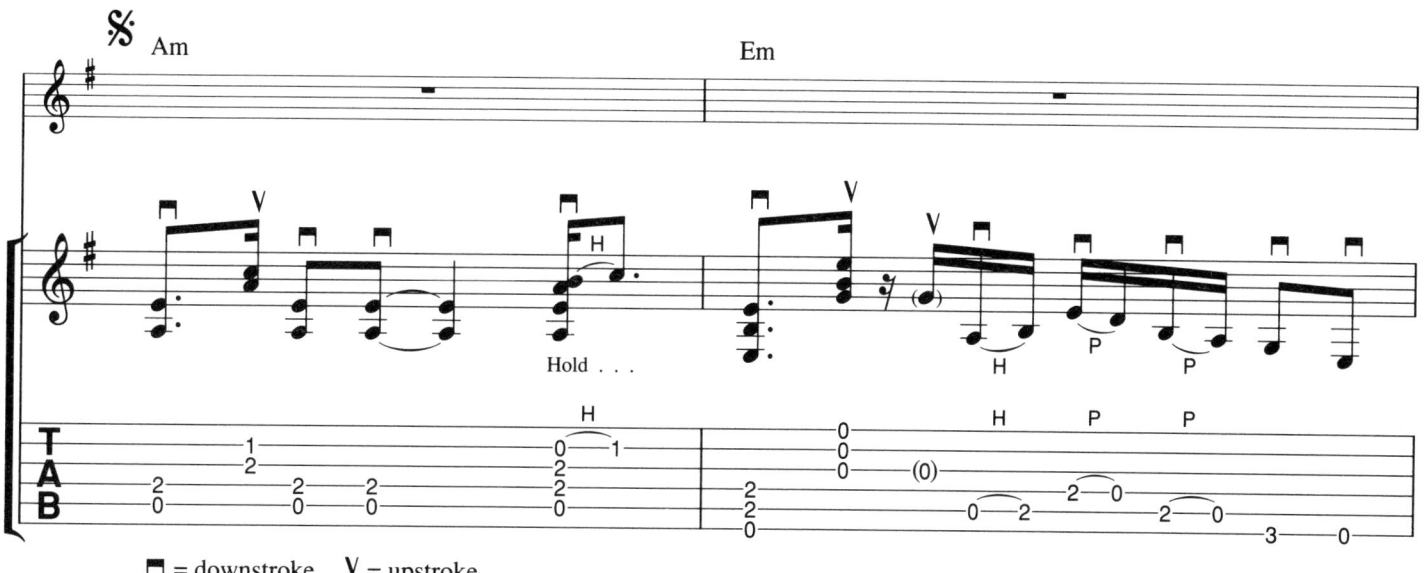

☐ = downstroke   V = upstroke

Verse:

1.   I don't care____   how long   this   lasts,   we   have   no   fut - ure,

See Block Lyrics for Verses 2&3 (%)

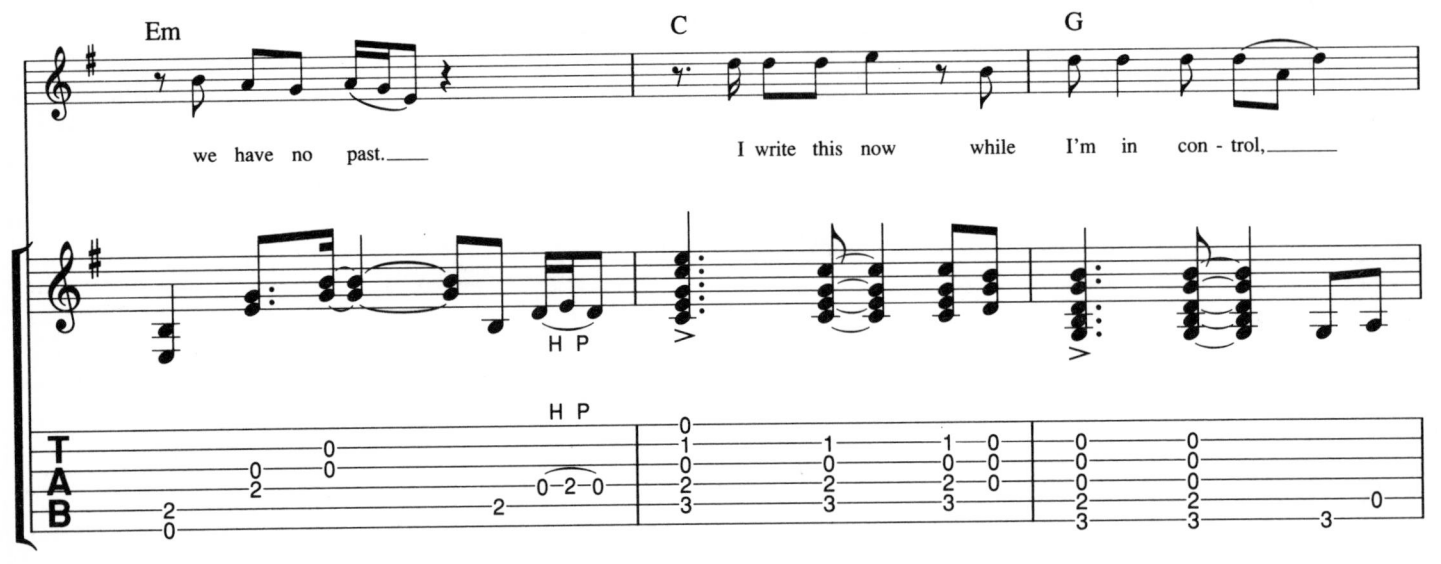

we have no past.____   I write this now   while   I'm   in   con - trol,____

I'll choose the words____   and now the mel - o - dy goes.   run through that   I'd

Chorus:

run   through.____   And I   miss you so,   and   I

Hold . . . .

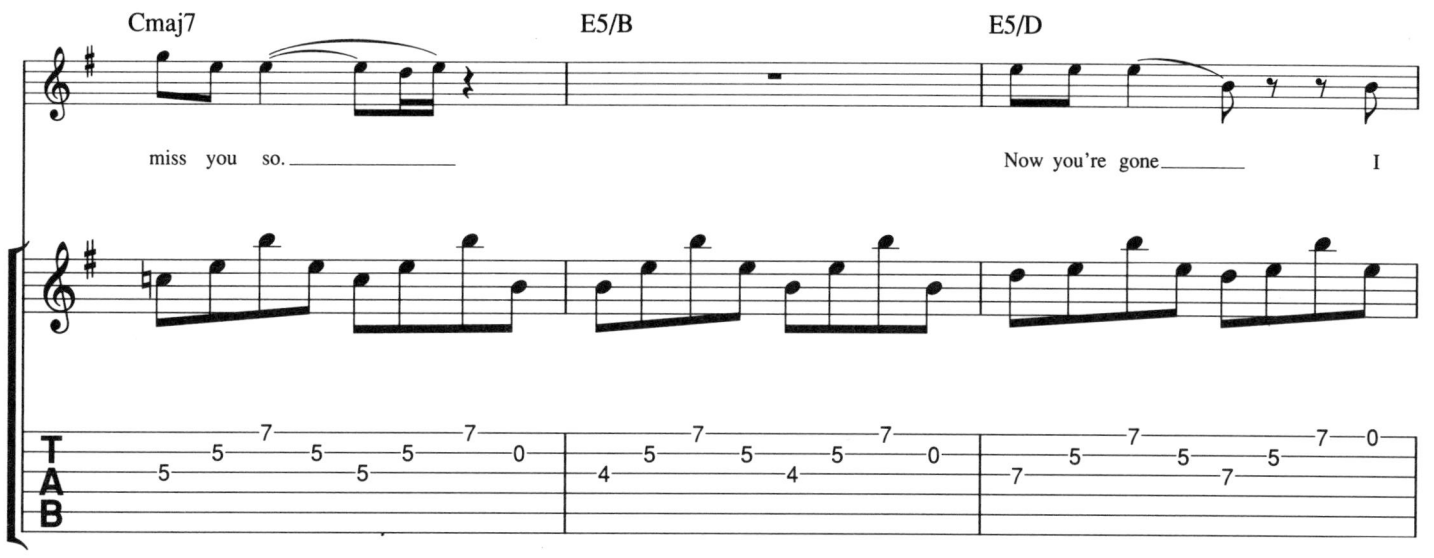

miss you so._____   Now you're gone_____   I

feel so a-lone,_____   oh,_____   I miss you so._____ (I do)

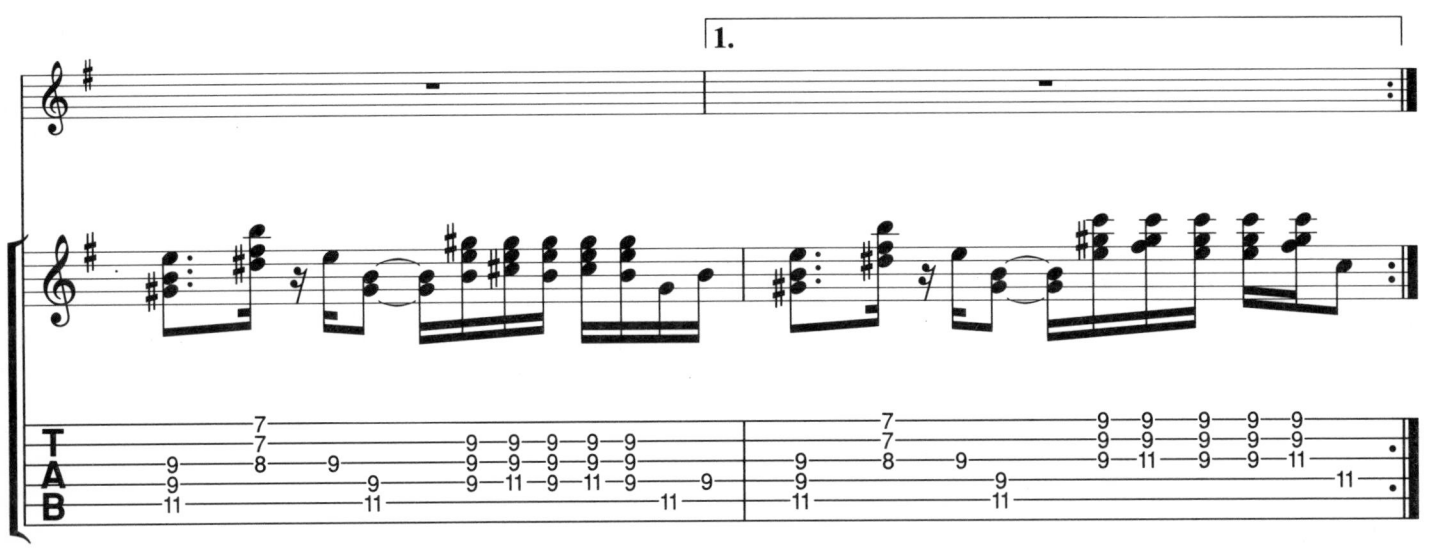

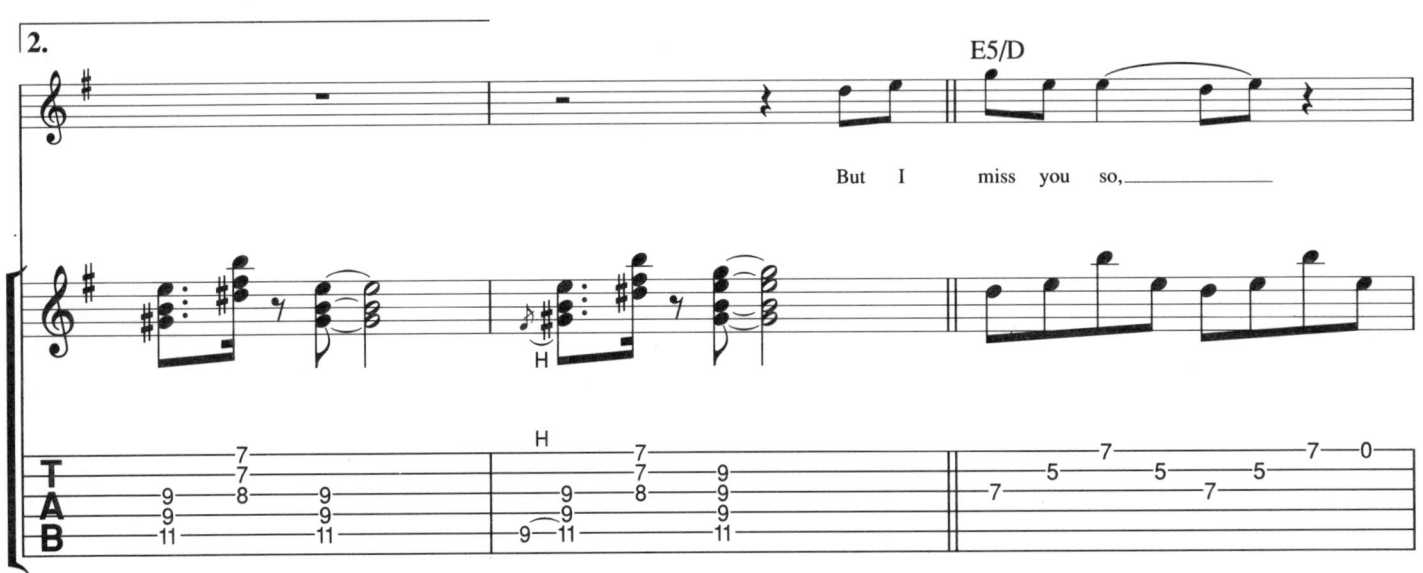

But I   miss you so,_____

oh,_____   but and I   miss you so. ____

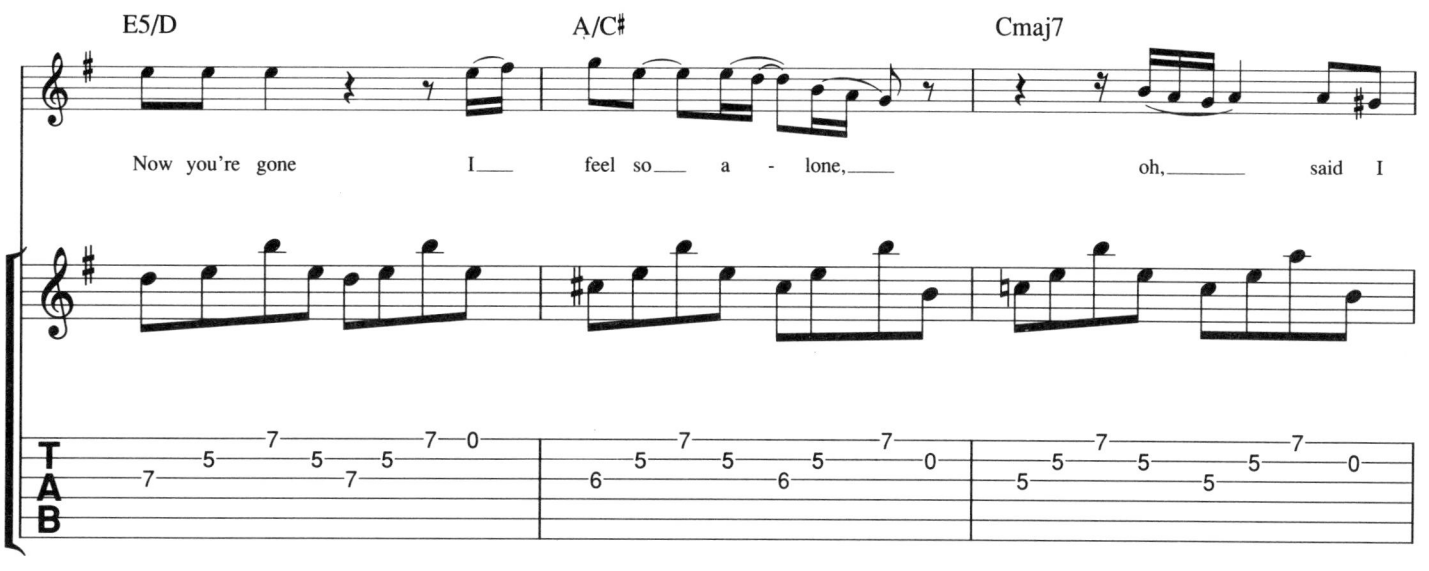

Now you're gone   I____ feel so____ a - lone,____   oh,_____ said I

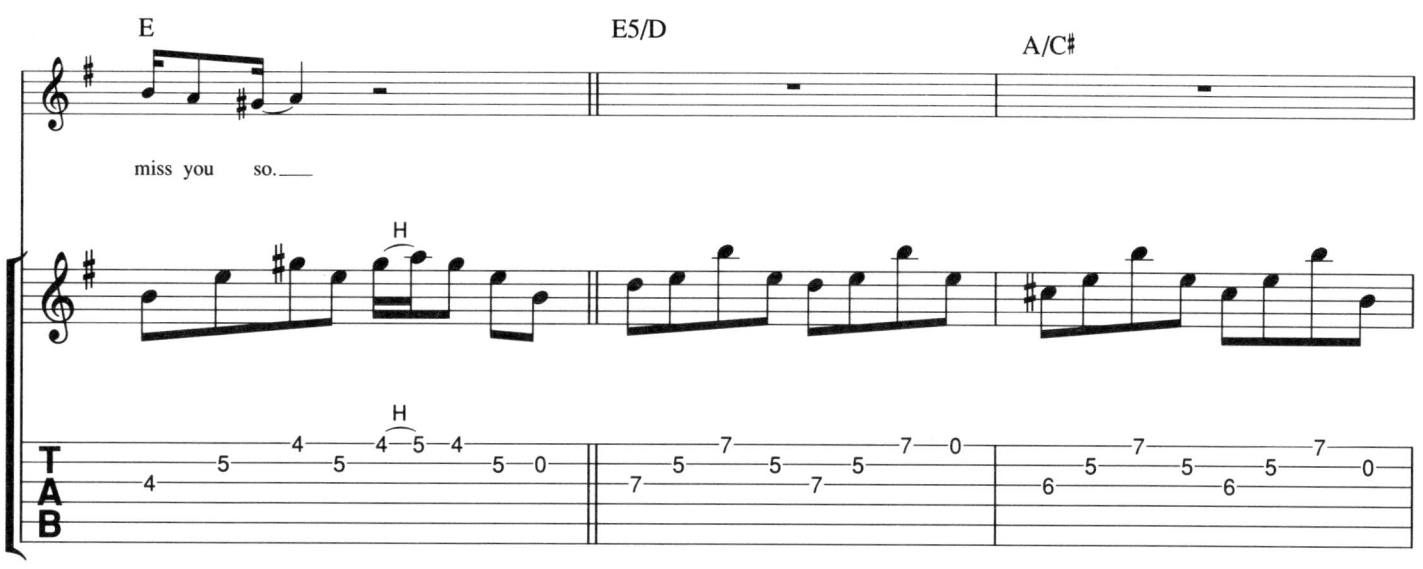

miss you so.____

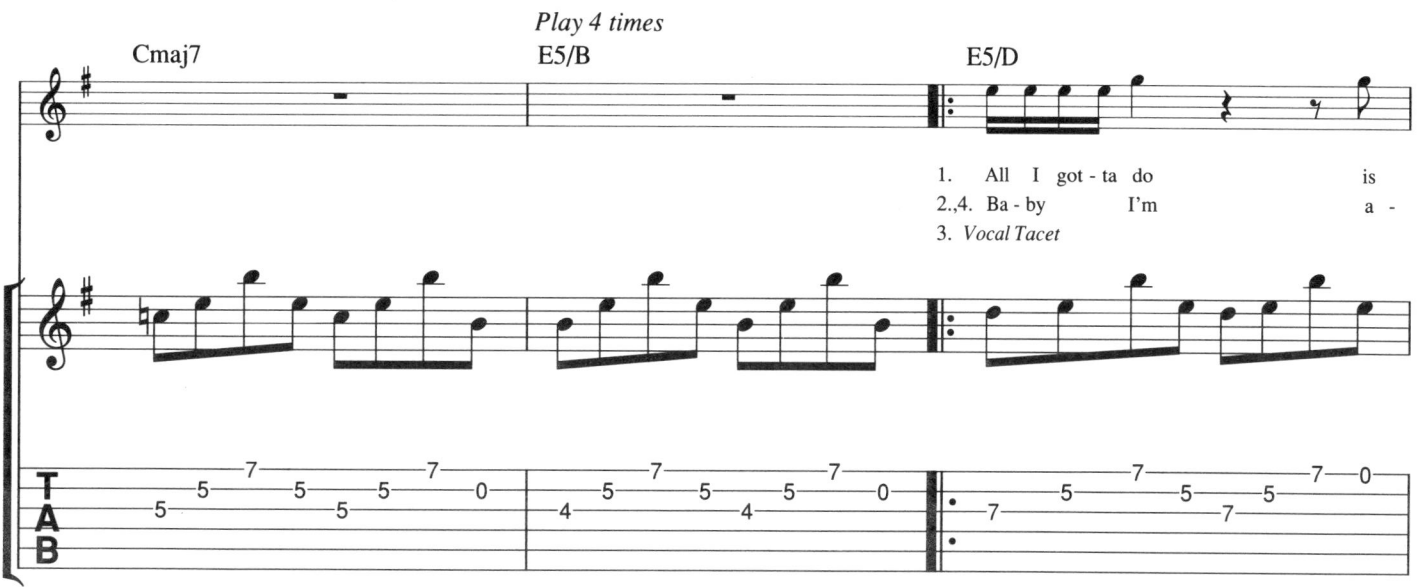

Play 4 times

1.   All I got - ta do   is
2.,4. Ba - by   I'm   a -
3. *Vocal Tacet*

think of you,_____ oh,_____ and I miss you so._____
-fraid to say why_____ oh,_____ and I

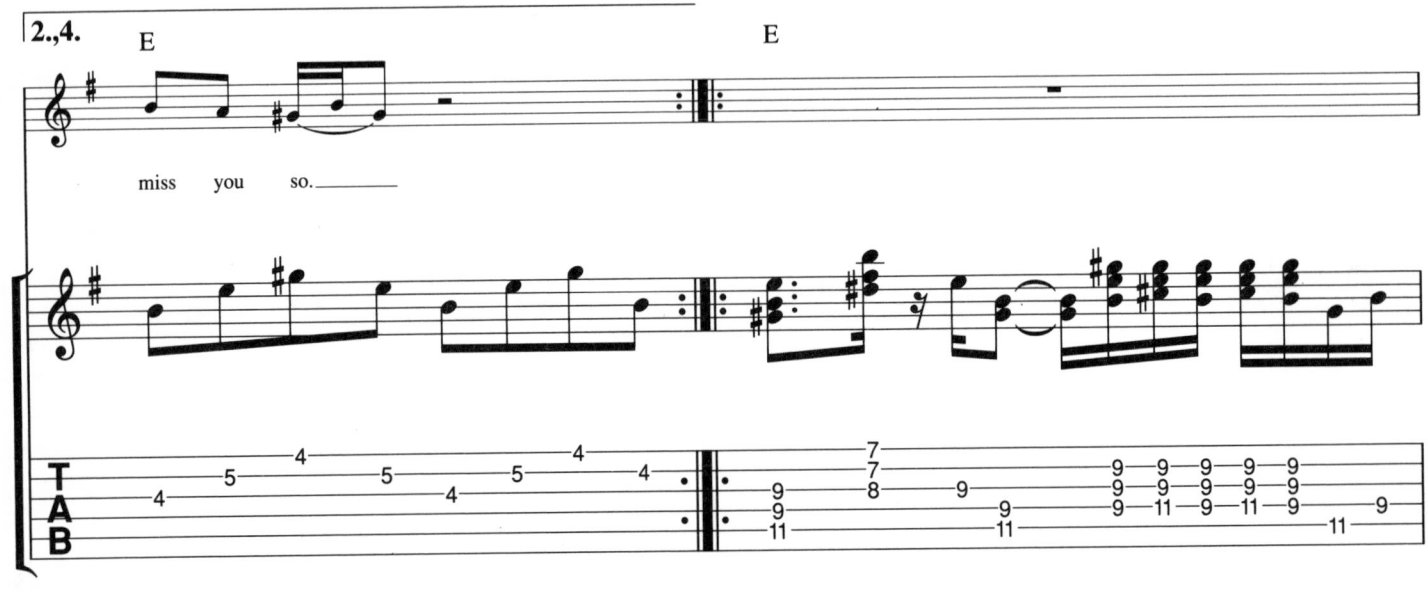

miss you so._____

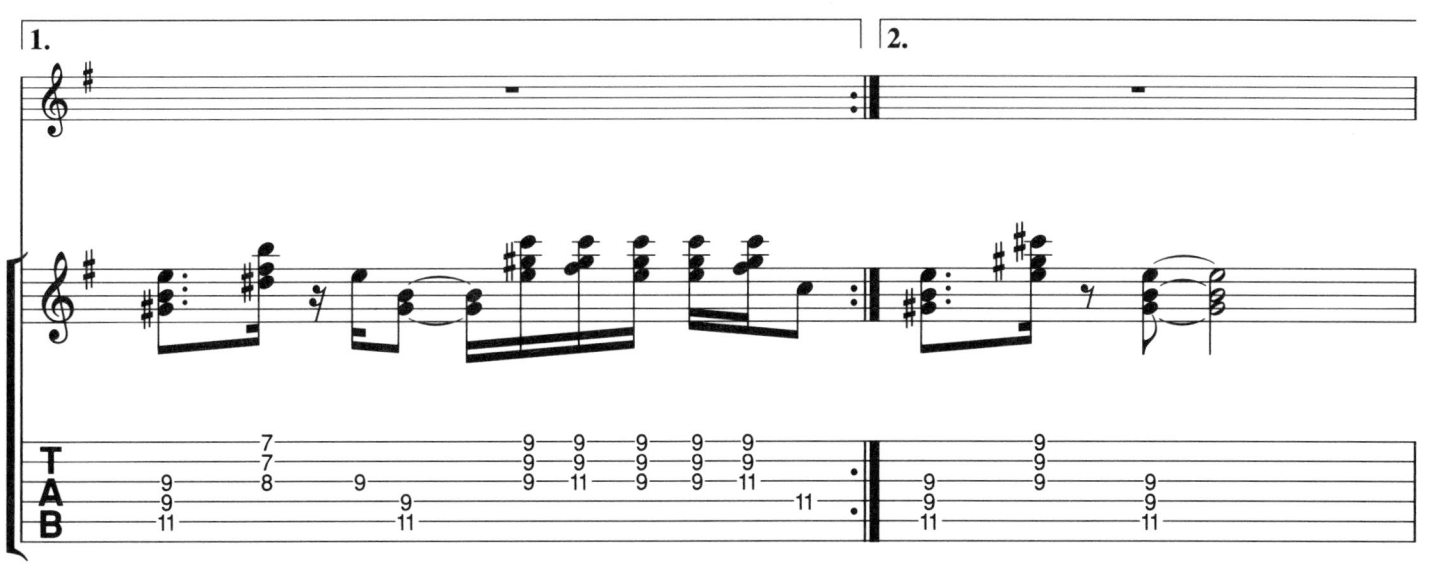

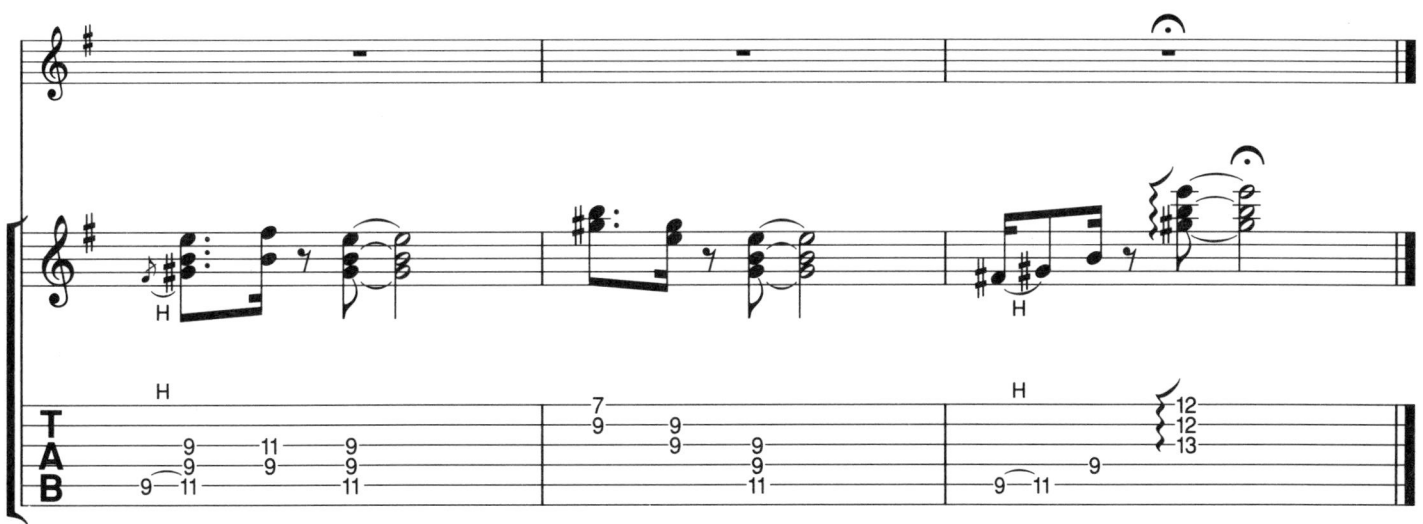

Verse 2:
Along winding streets we walked hand in hand
And how I long for that sharp wind to take my breath away again
I'd run my fingers through your hair
Hair like a wheatfield, I'd run through.

Verse 3(𝄋)
I'd seed you a flower, a sunflower bright
While you cloud my days, messing up my nights
And all the way up to the top of your head
Sun-shower kisses I felt we had.

time passes...

words & music by paul weller

hid my face,____ it's hard to trace____ these feel - ings._____

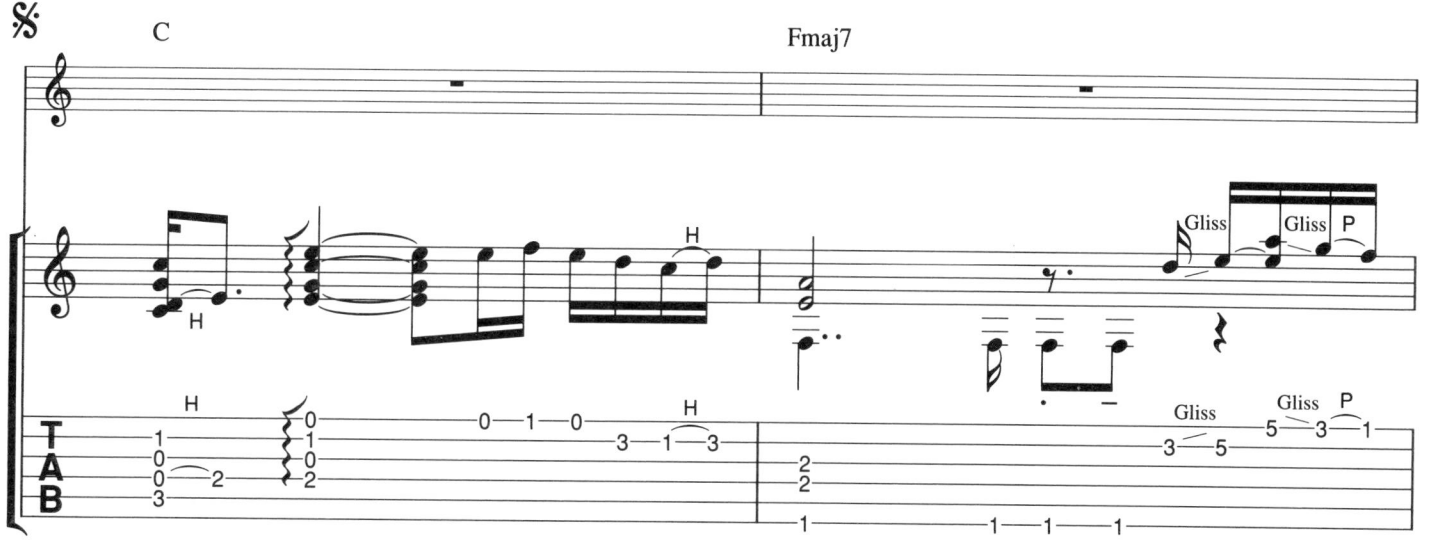

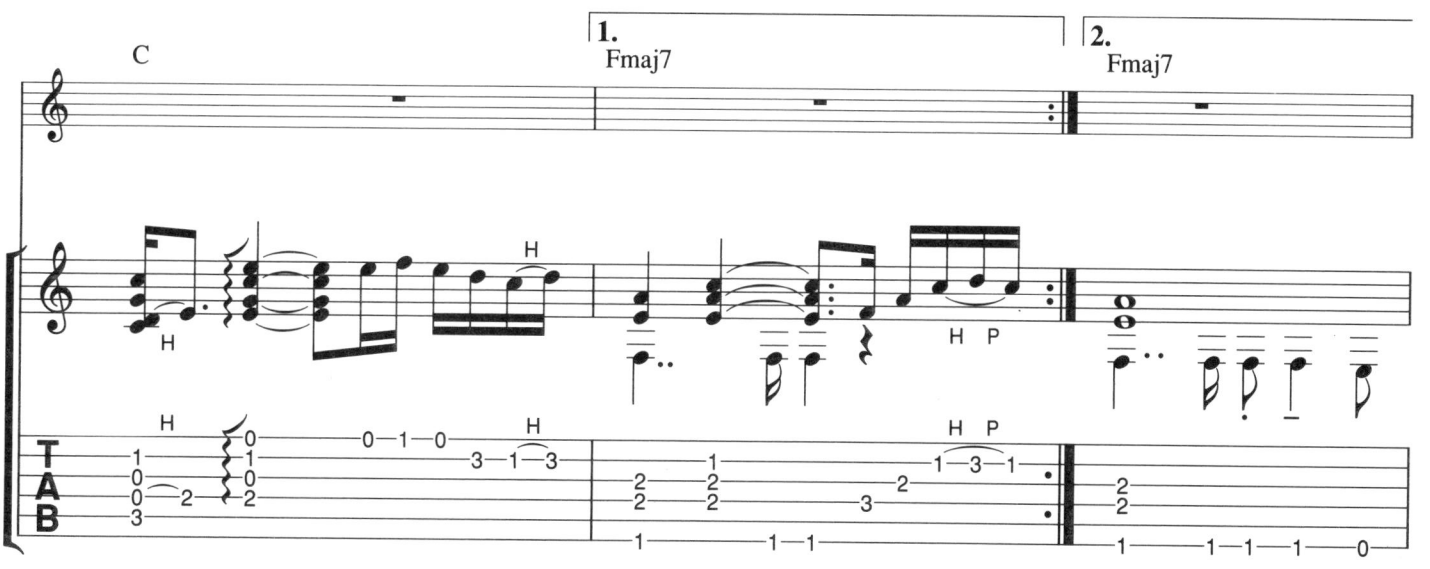

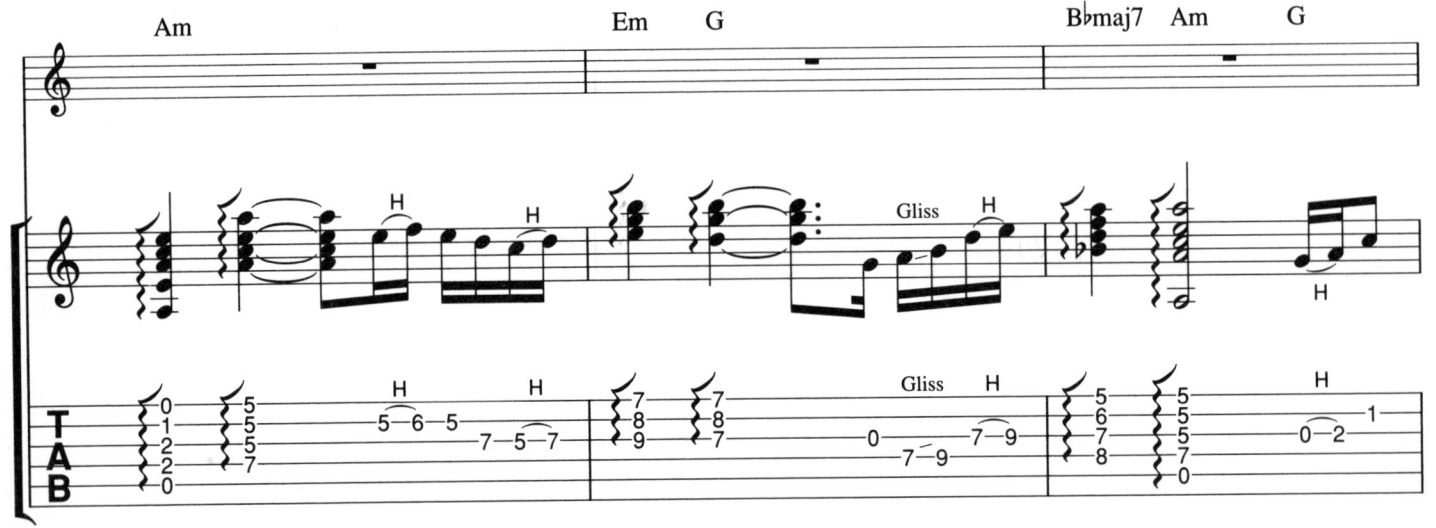

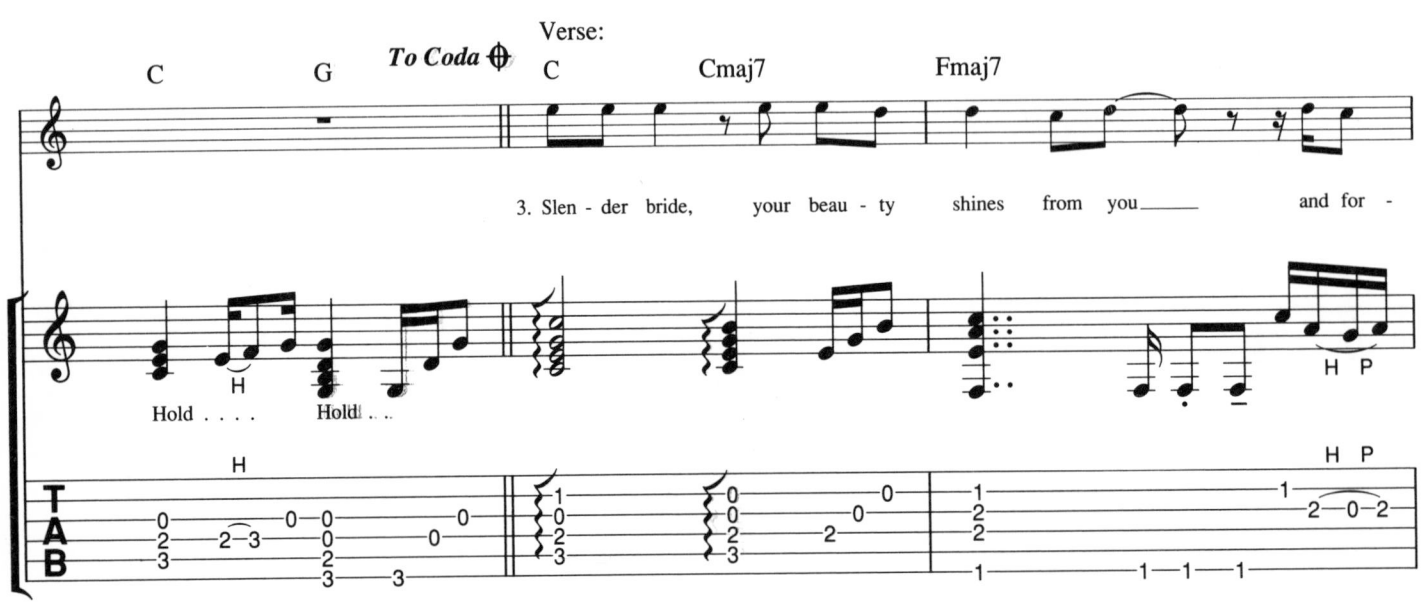

3. Slen - der bride, your beau - ty shines from you____ and for -

ev - er more I'll be on___ your side for sure.____ A light in your life____ that al - ways

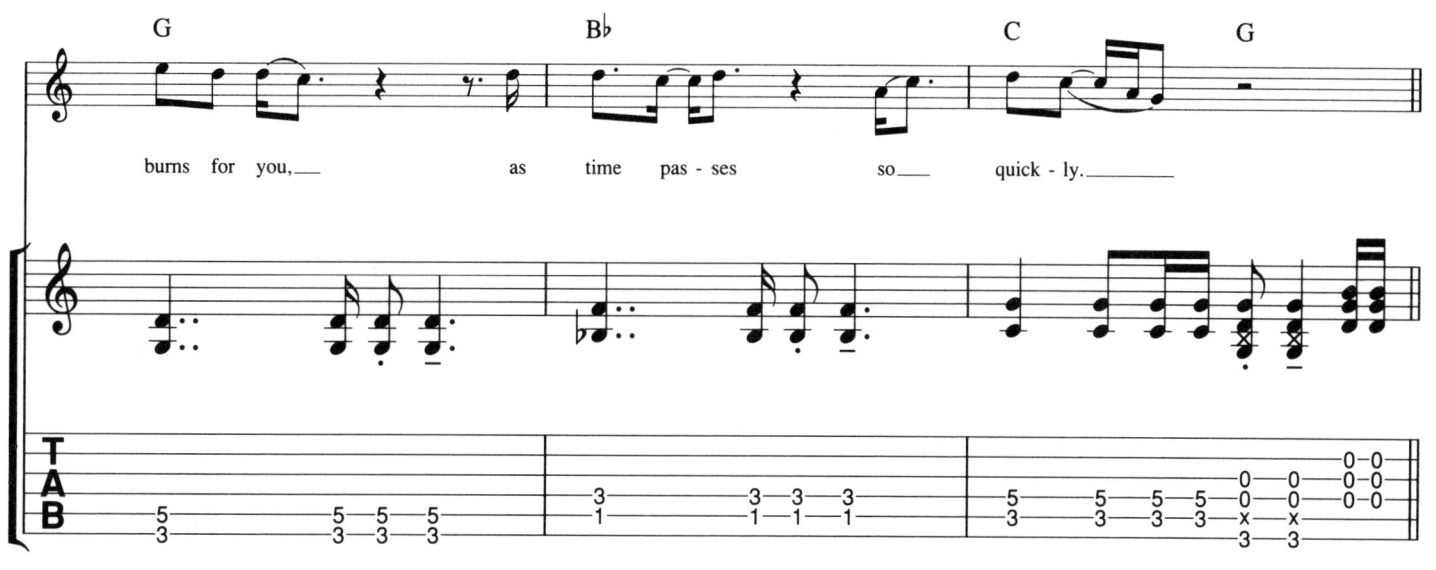

burns for you, as time pas-ses so_ quick-ly._

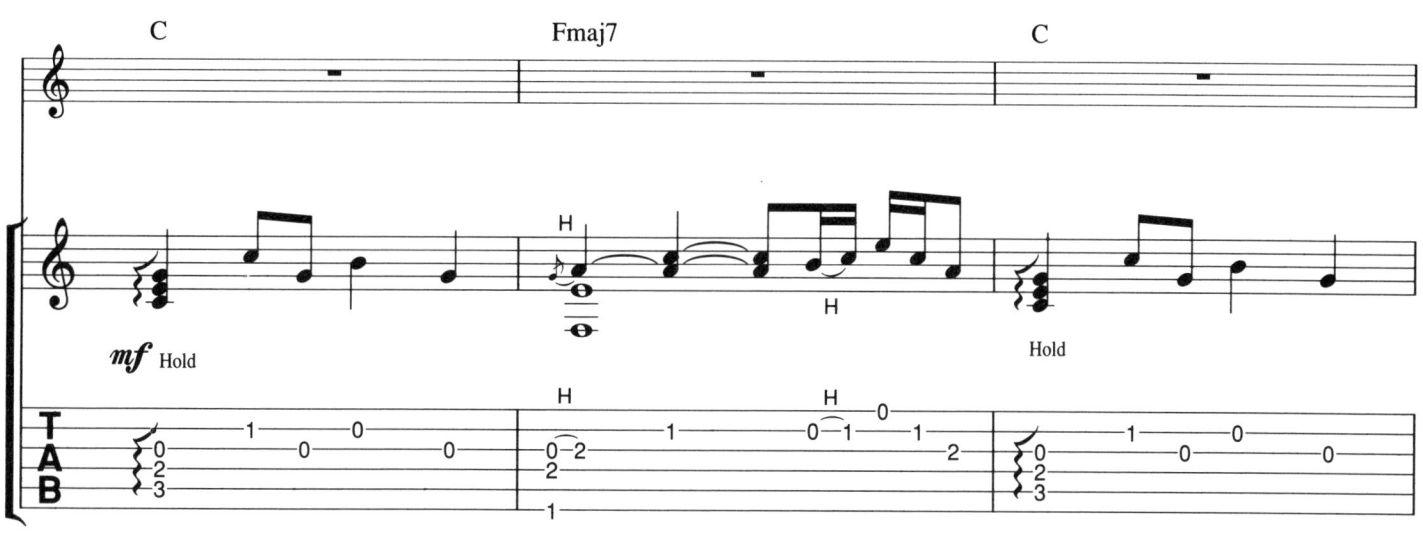

Verse:

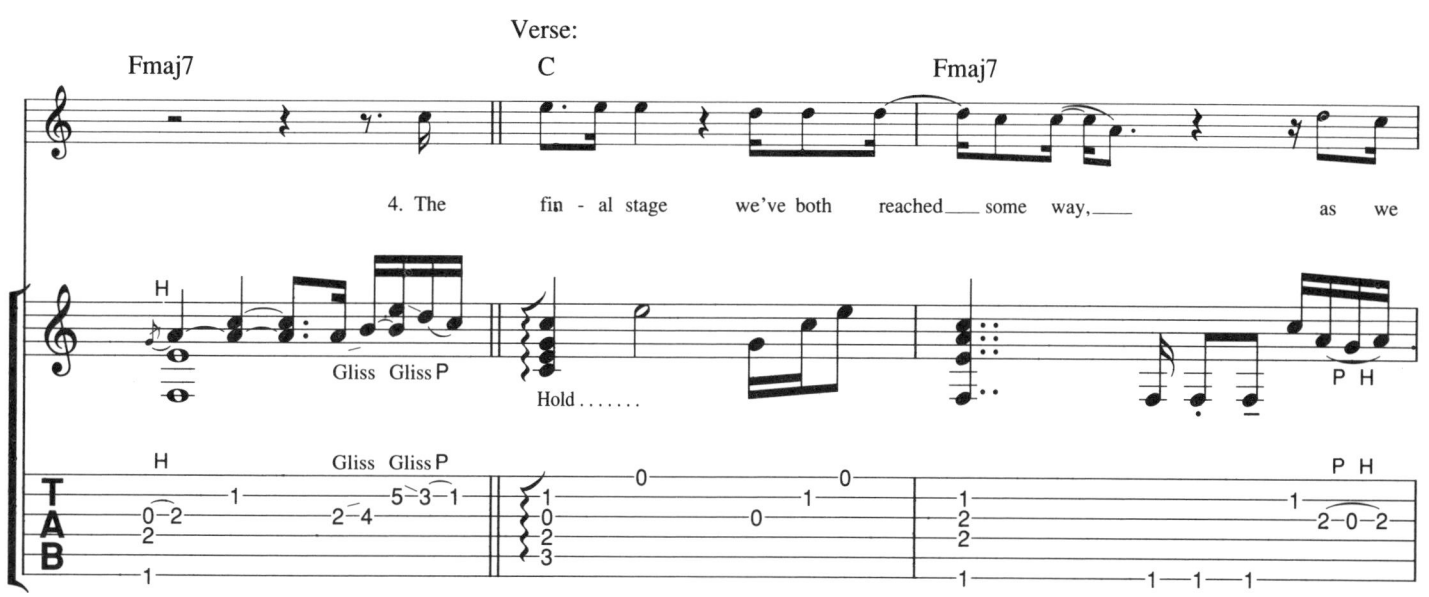

4. The fin-al stage we've both reached_ some way,_ as we

board our train to differ-ent sta-tions.___ And the parts we__ play___ and the

D. 𝄋 al ⨁ Coda

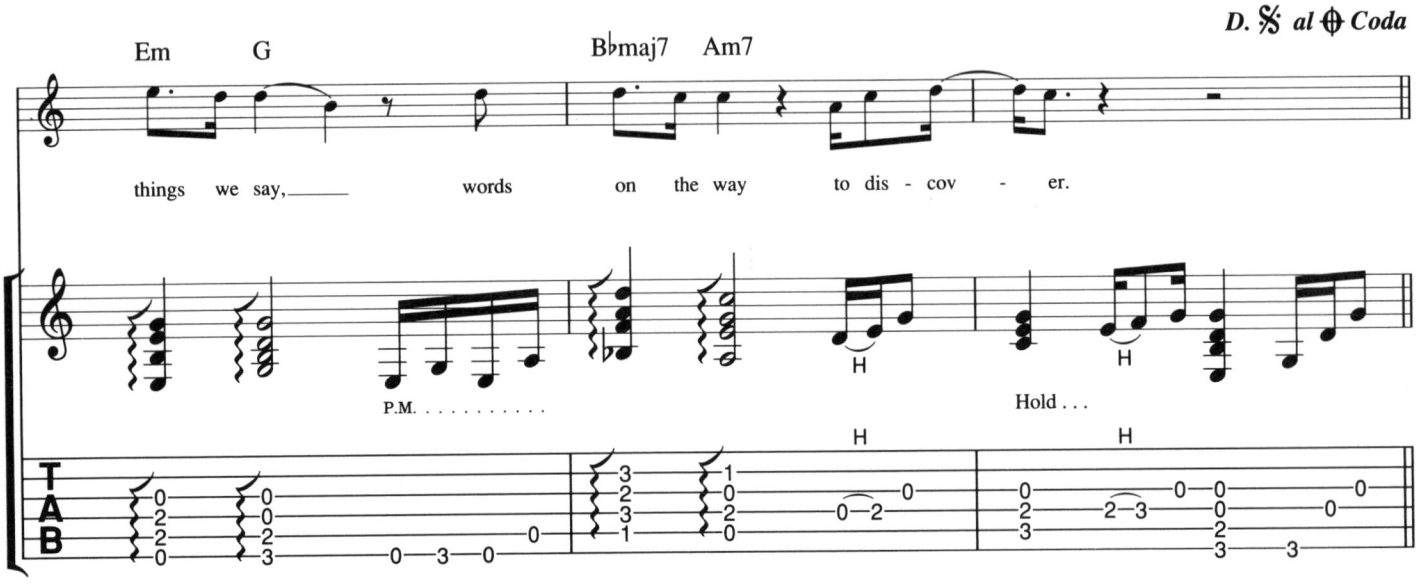

things we say,___ words on the way to dis-cov - er.

P.M. . . . . Hold . . .

Coda ⨁

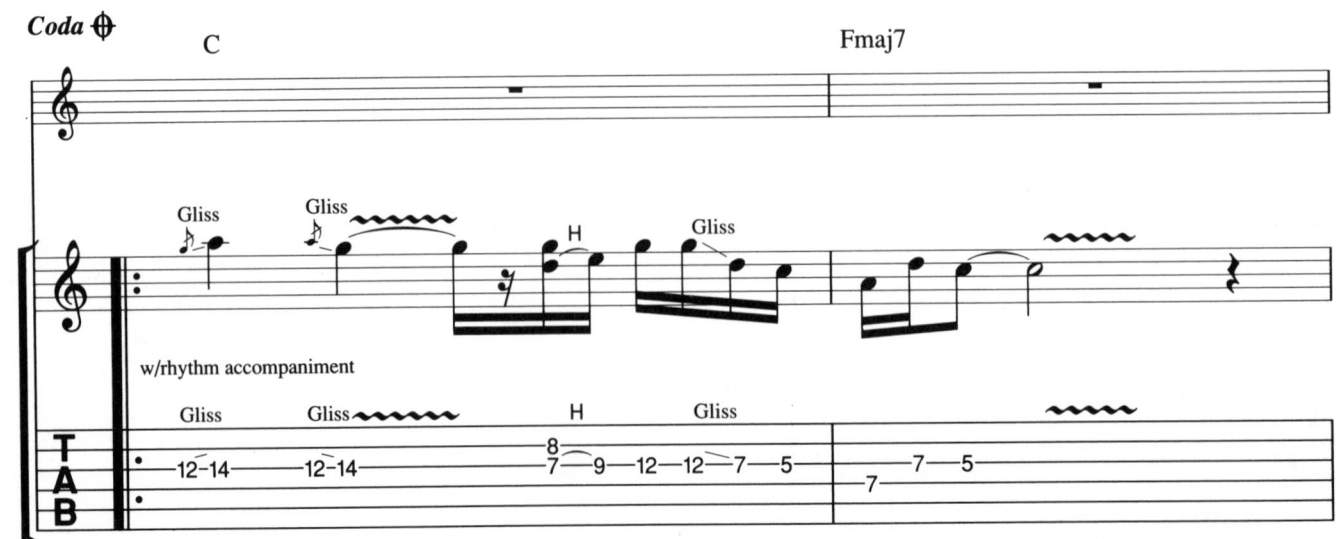

w/rhythm accompaniment

Verse 2:
Gone so soon, the time I spent with you
Like an old, old tune keep running through my head
I wanted to say so many things
But my mouth went dry and one word and I'd cry.

wild wood

words & music by paul weller

П = downstroke   V = upstroke

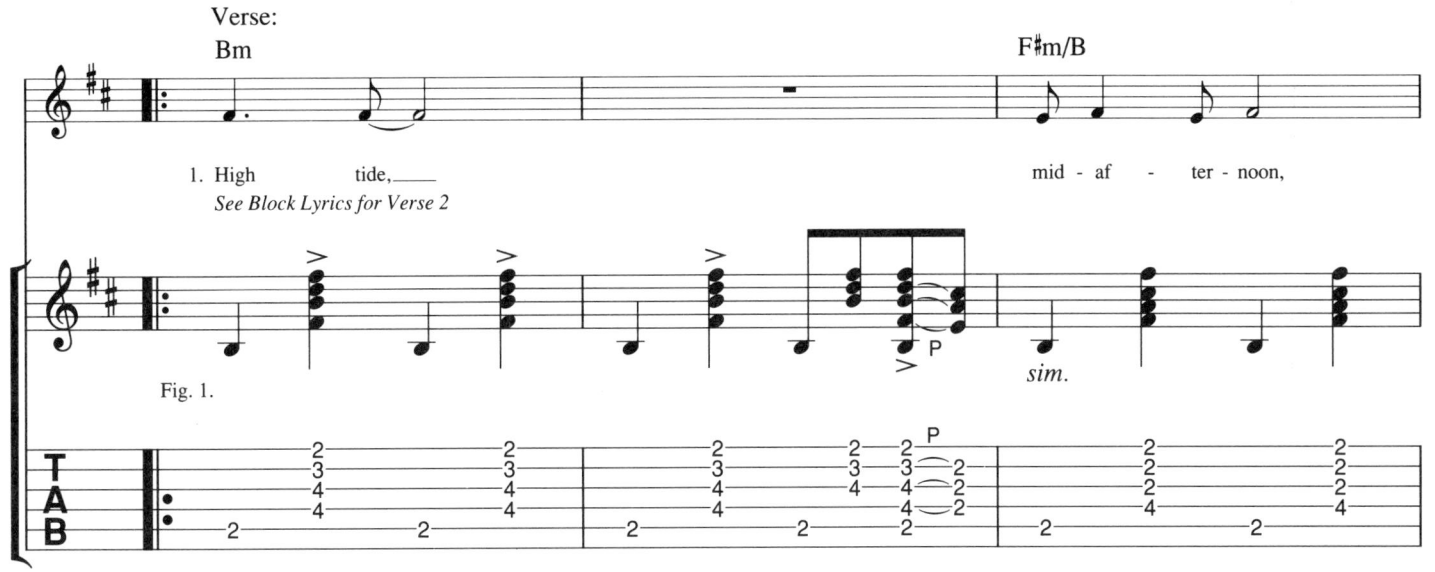

Verse:

1. High tide,_____ mid - af - ter - noon,

See Block Lyrics for Verse 2

Fig. 1.

peo - ple fly by

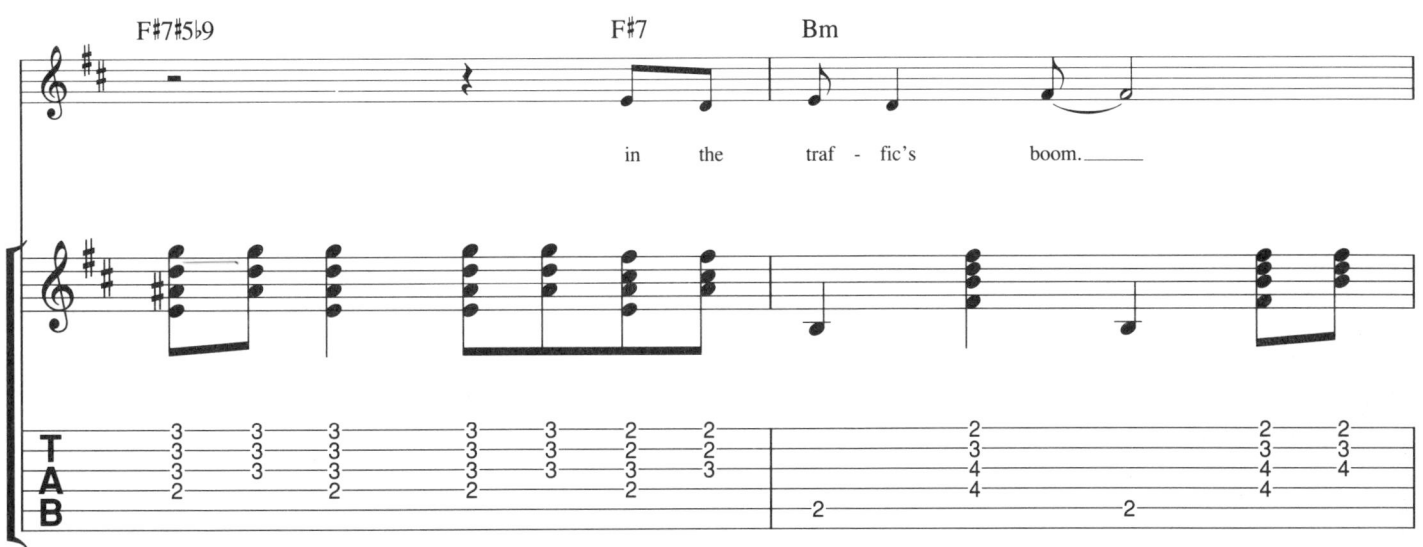

in the traf - fic's boom._____

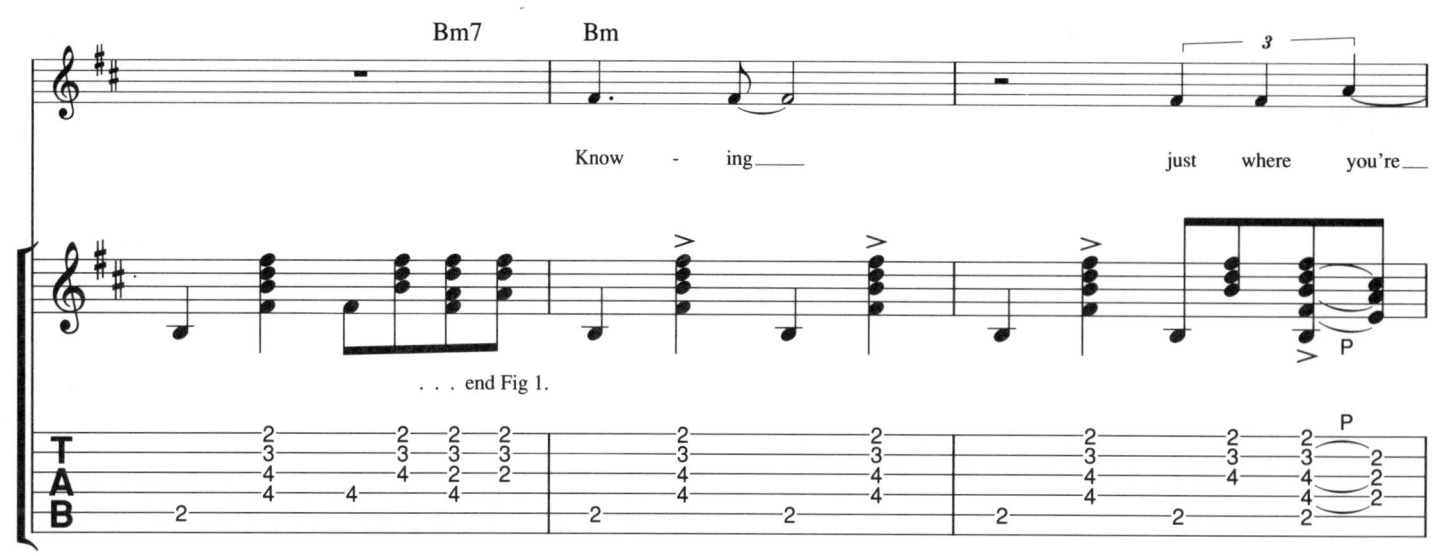

Know - ing____ just where you're____

. . . end Fig 1.

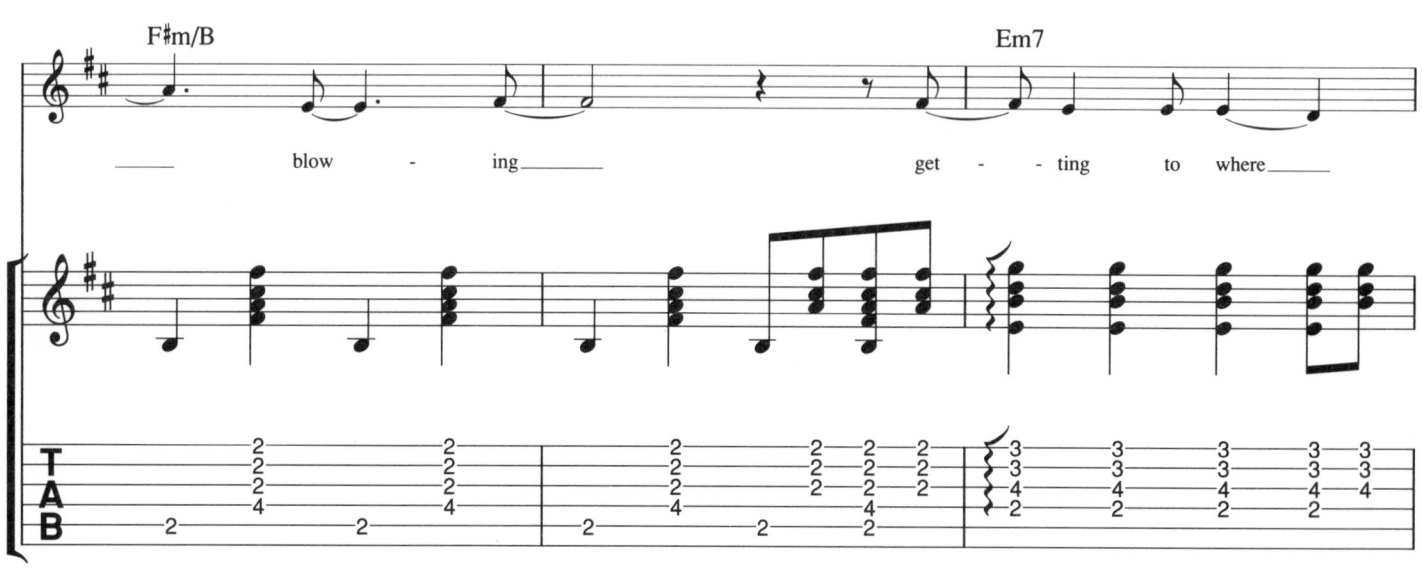

____ blow - ing_____ get - - ting to where____

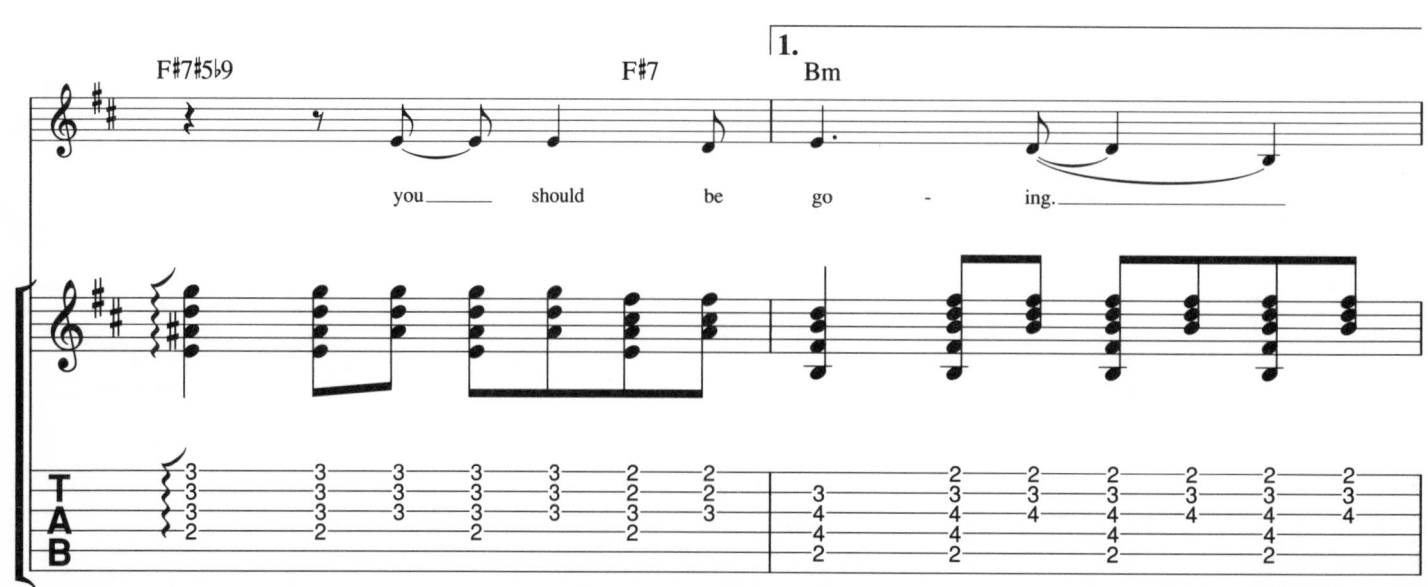

you____ should be go - ing._____

1. *cont'd*

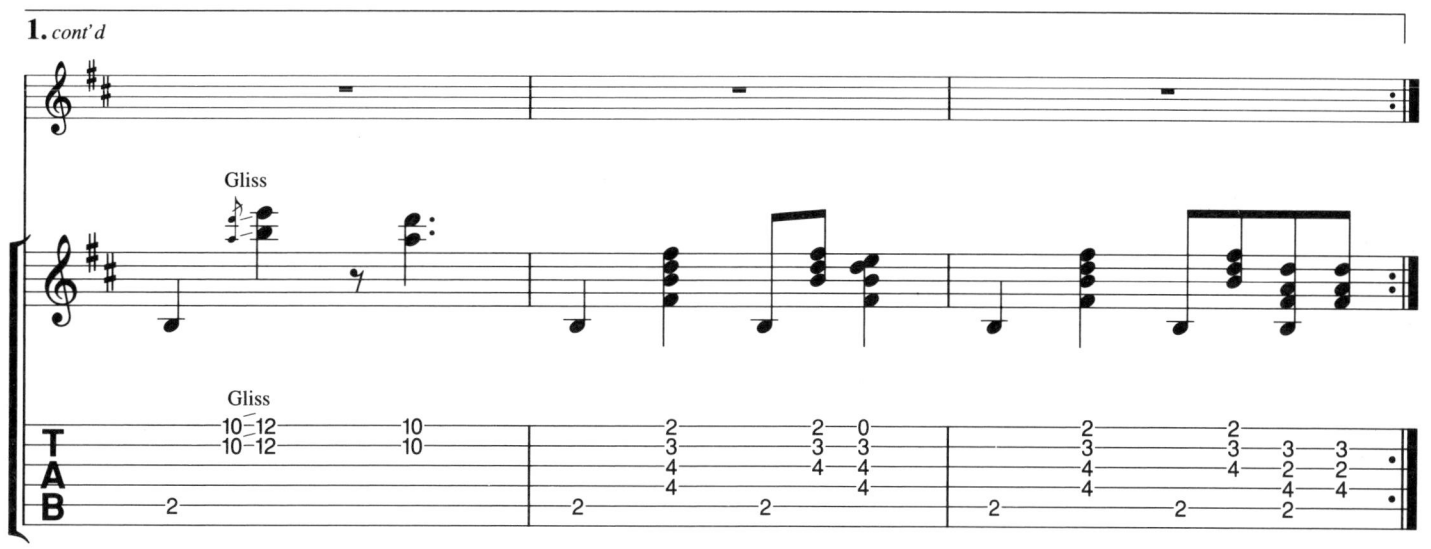

2.

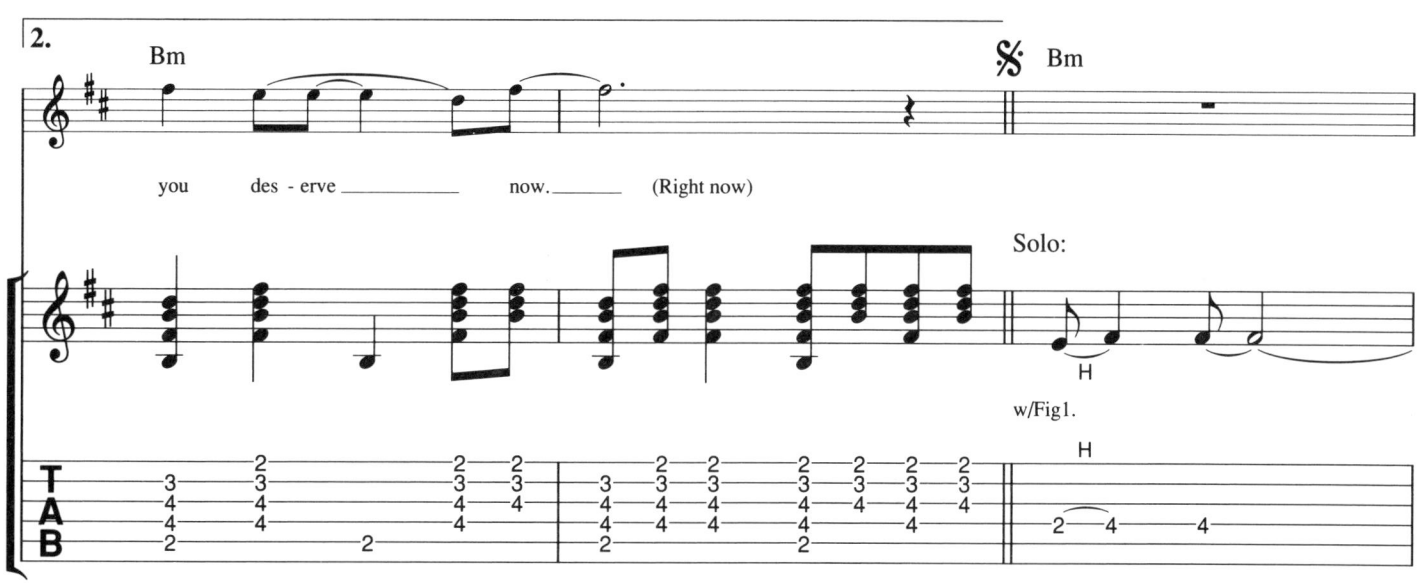

you   des - erve _____ now. _____ (Right now)

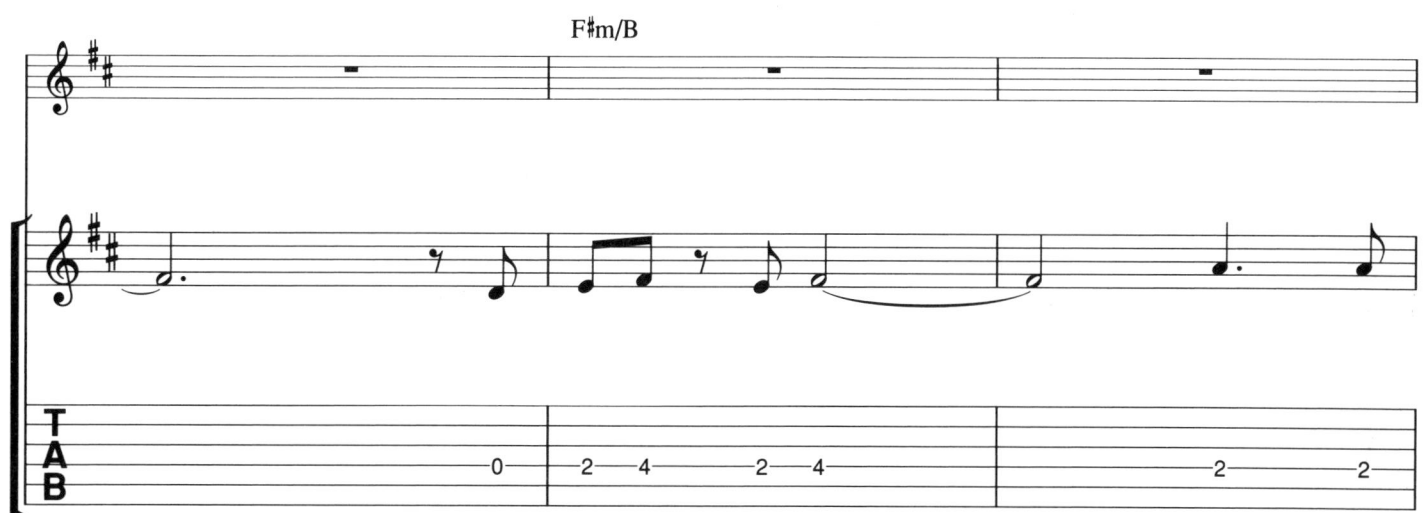

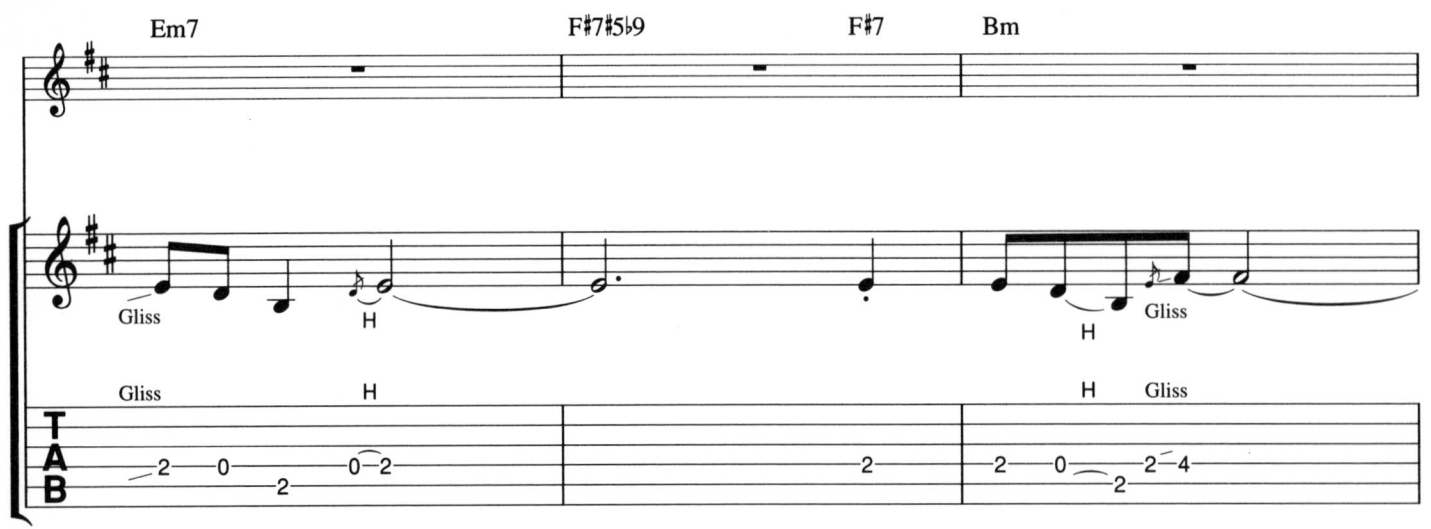

Verse:

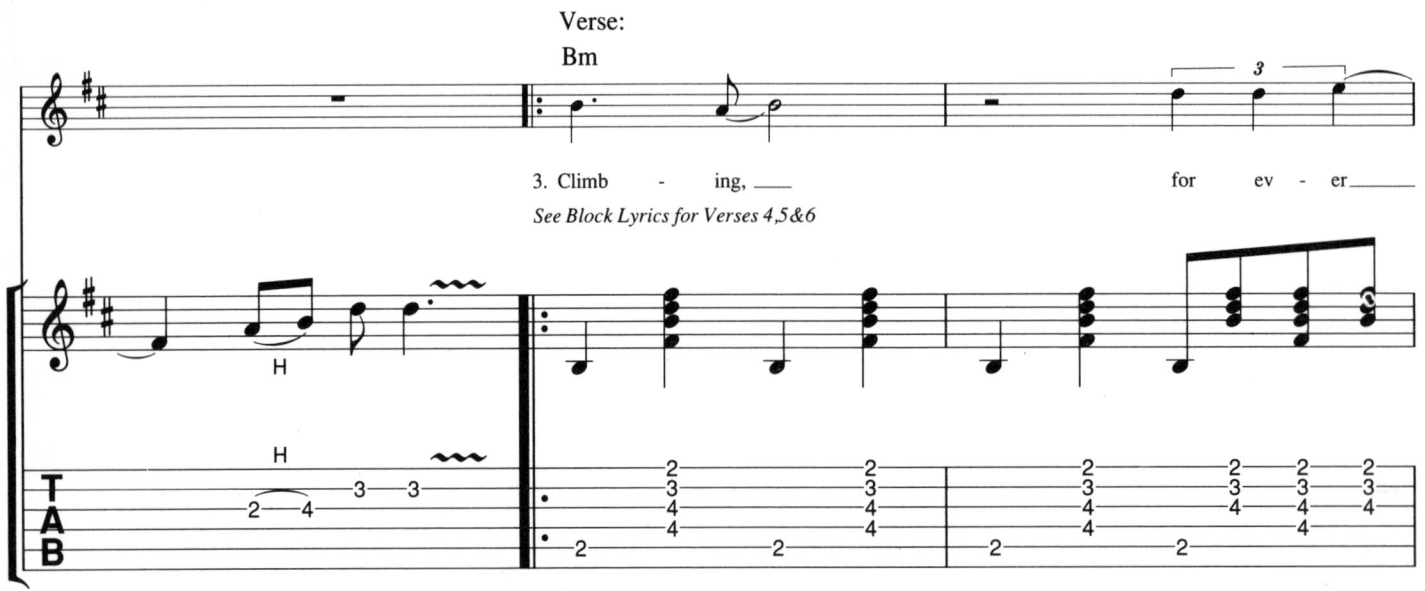

3. Climb - ing, _____ for - ev - er _____

See Block Lyrics for Verses 4,5&6

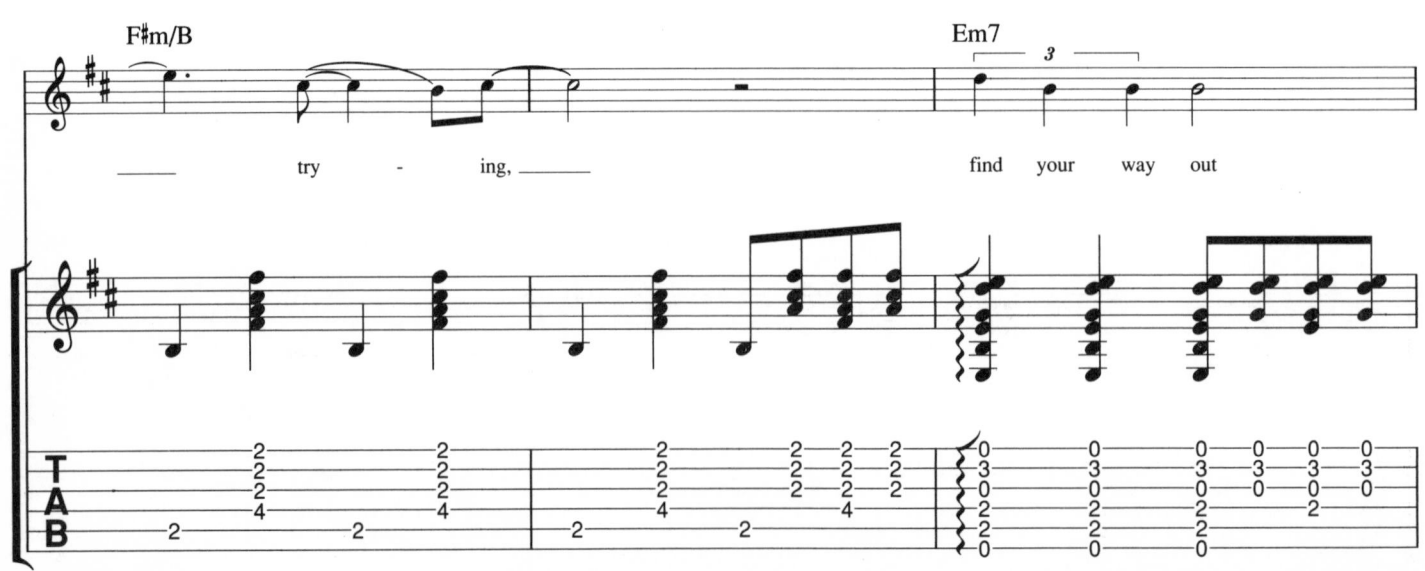

_____ try - ing, _____ find your way out

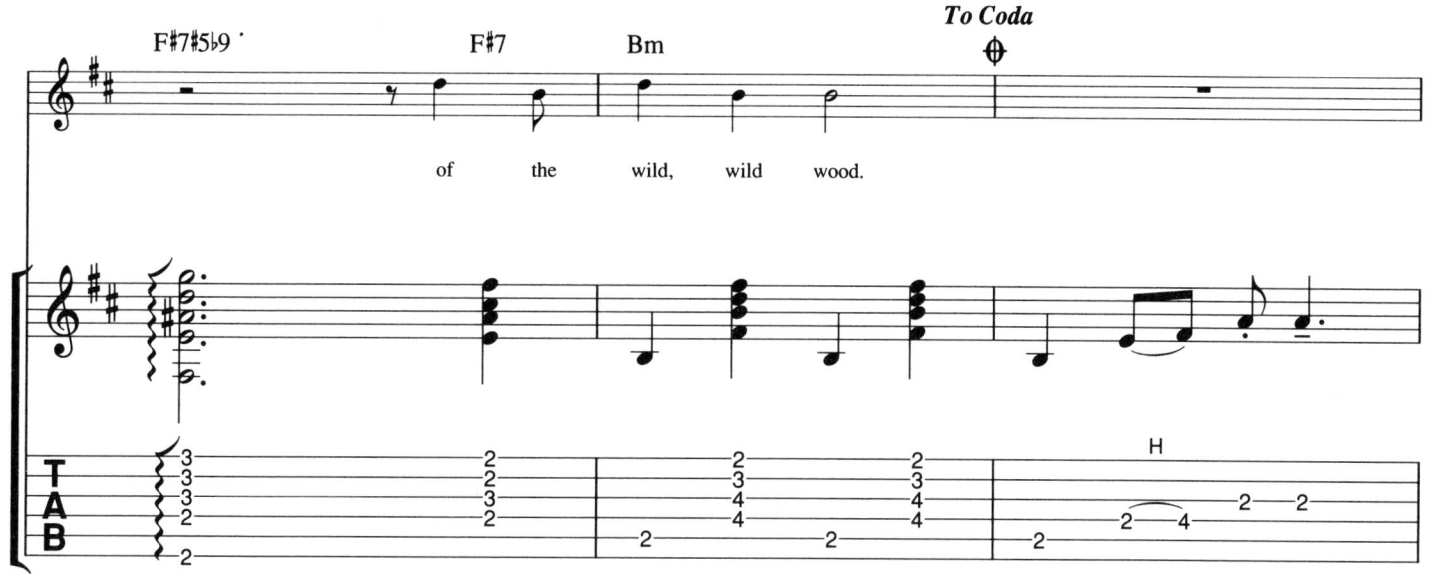

of the wild, wild wood.

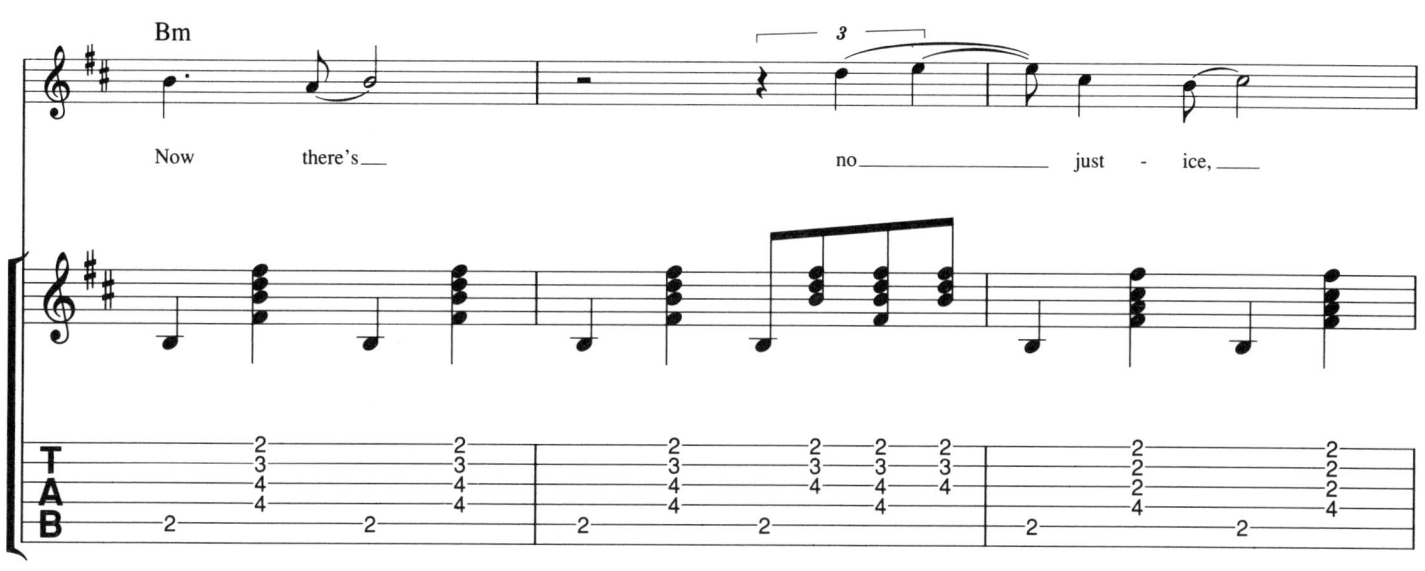

Now there's ___ no ___ just - ice, ___

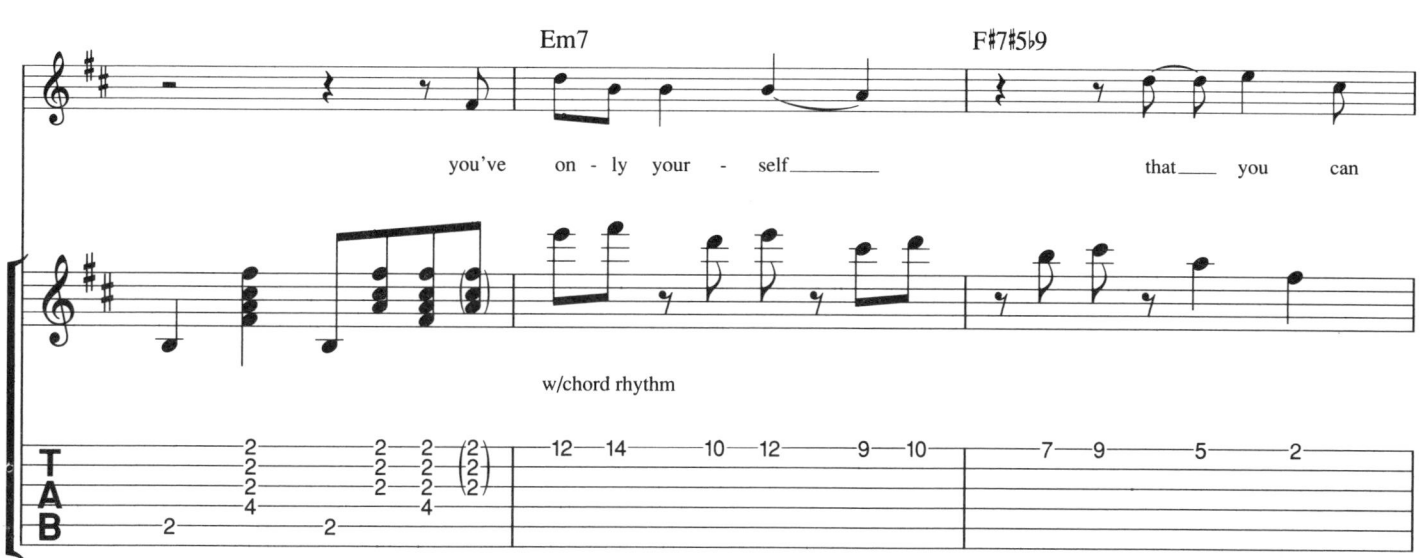

you've on - ly your - self ___ that ___ you can

w/chord rhythm

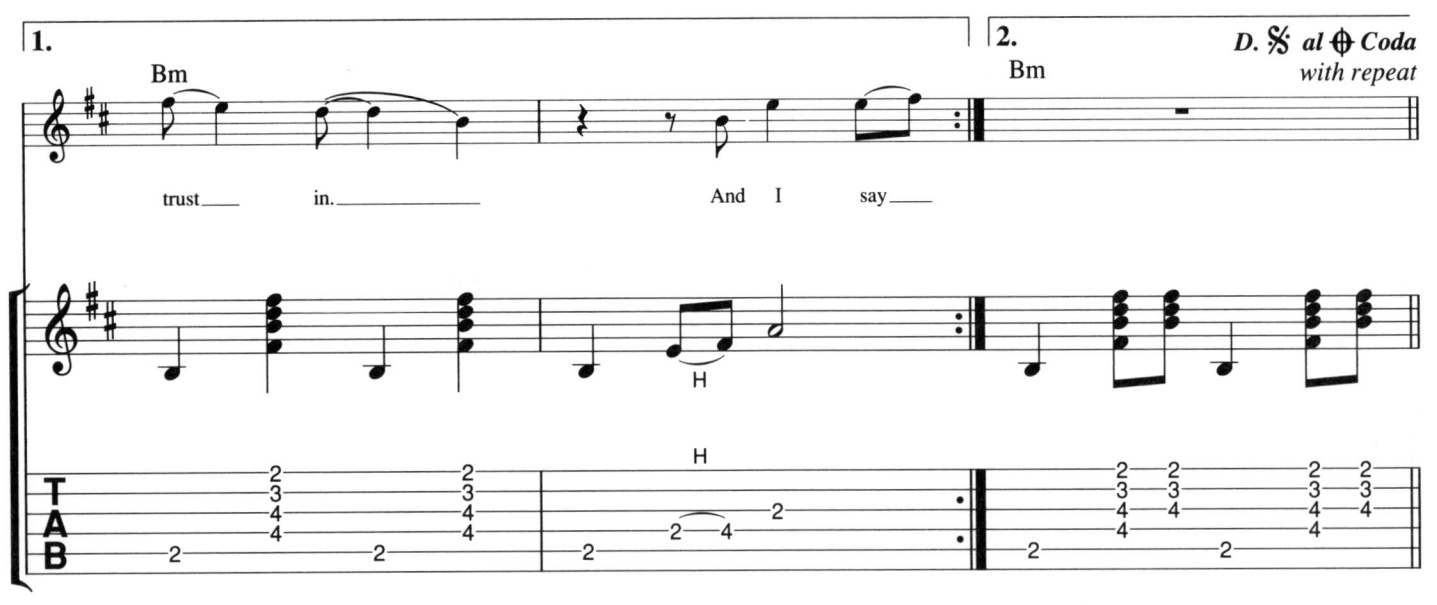

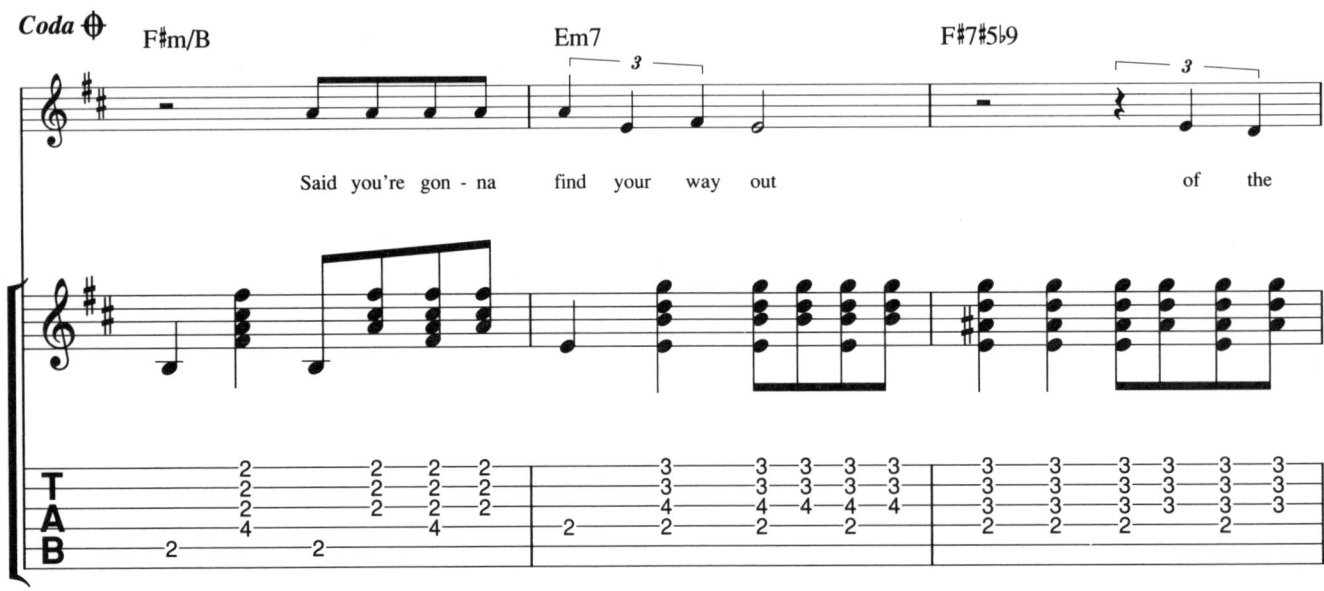

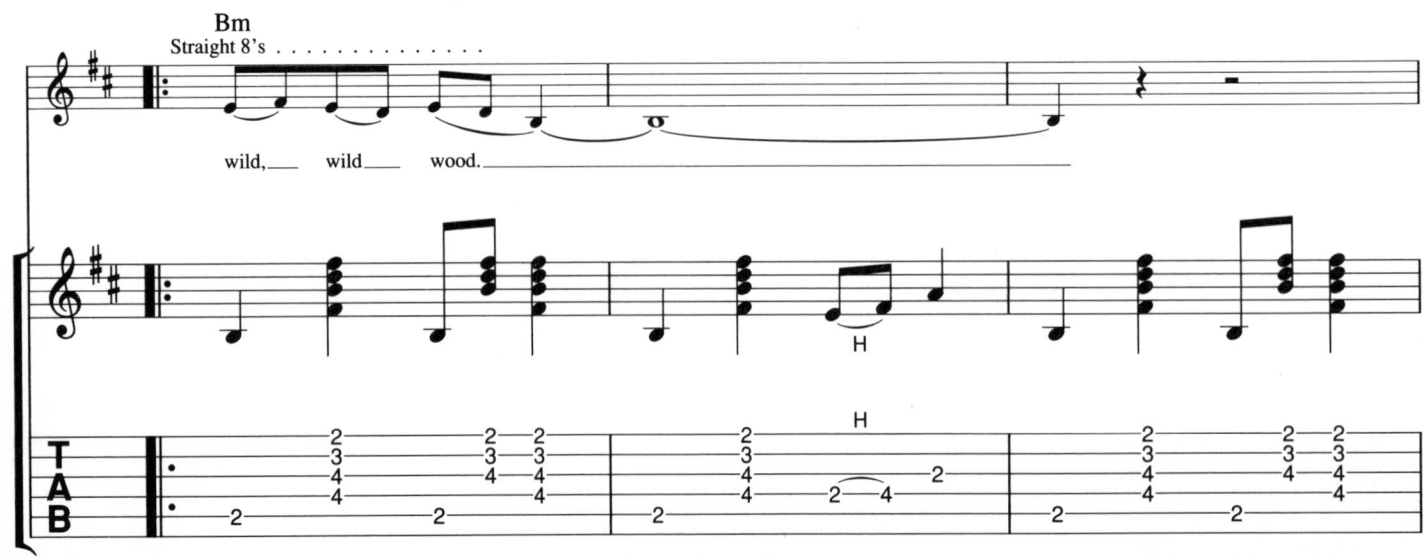

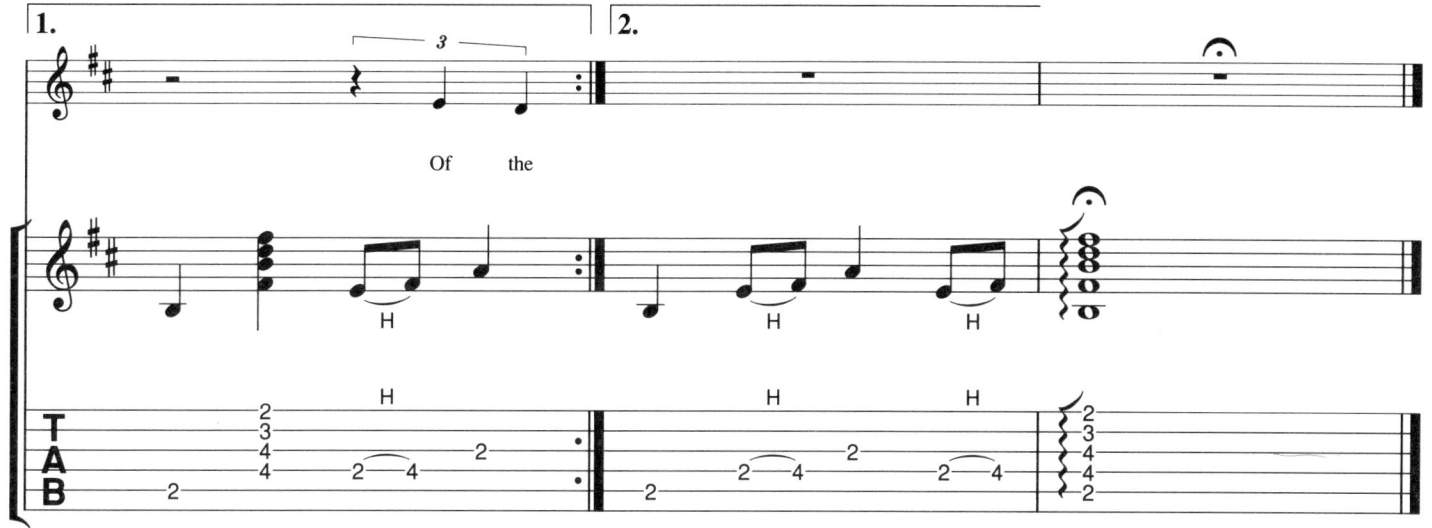

Of the

Verse 2:
Don't let them get you down
Making you feel guilty about
Golden rain will bring you riches
All the good things you deserve now.

Verse 4:
And I said high tide, mid-afternoon
People fly by in the traffic's boom
Knowing just where you're blowing
Getting to where you should be going.

Verse 5 (𝄋):
Day by day your world fades away
Waking to feel all the dreams that say
Golden rain will bring you riches
All the good things you deserve now.

Verse 6
And I say climbing, forever trying
You're gonna find your way out of the wild, wild wood.
(*To Coda*)

woodcutter's son

words & music by paul weller

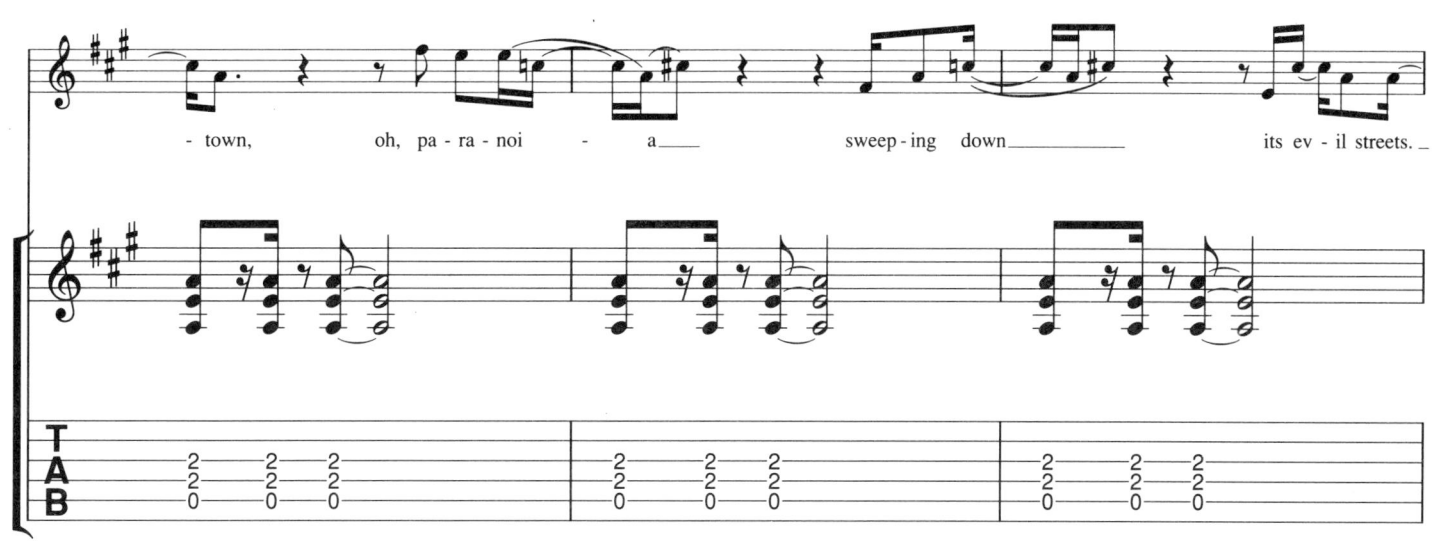

-town, oh, pa - ra - noi - a____ sweep - ing down_____ its ev - il streets._

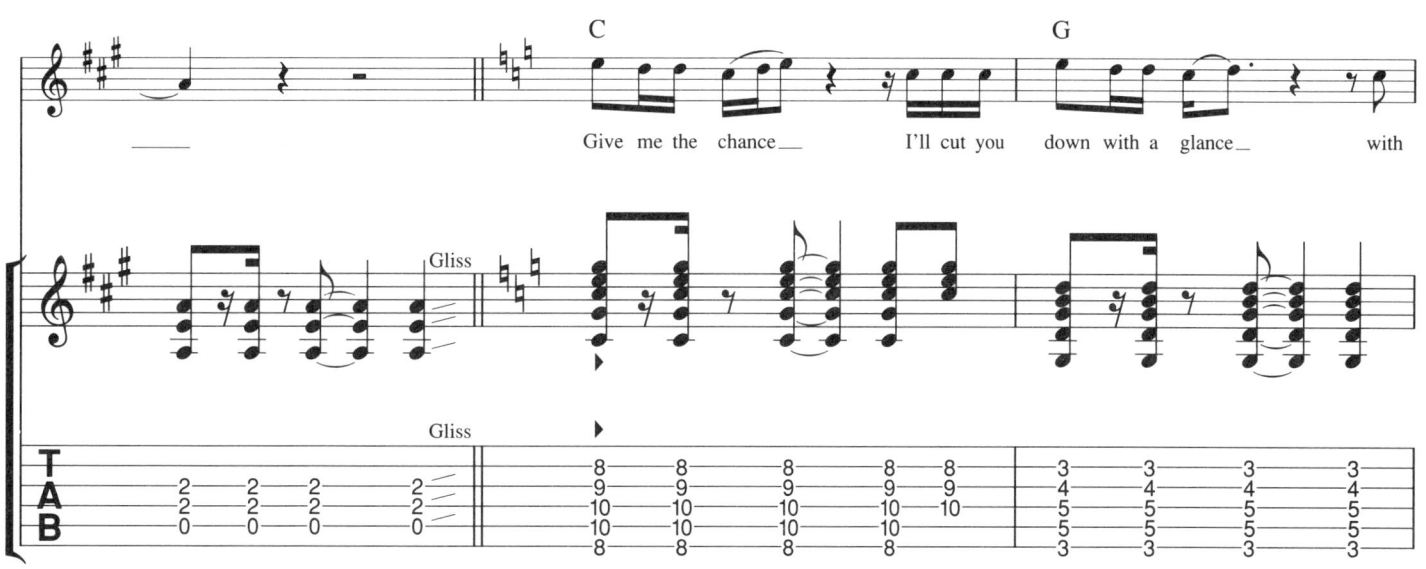

____ Give me the chance__ I'll cut you down with a glance__ with

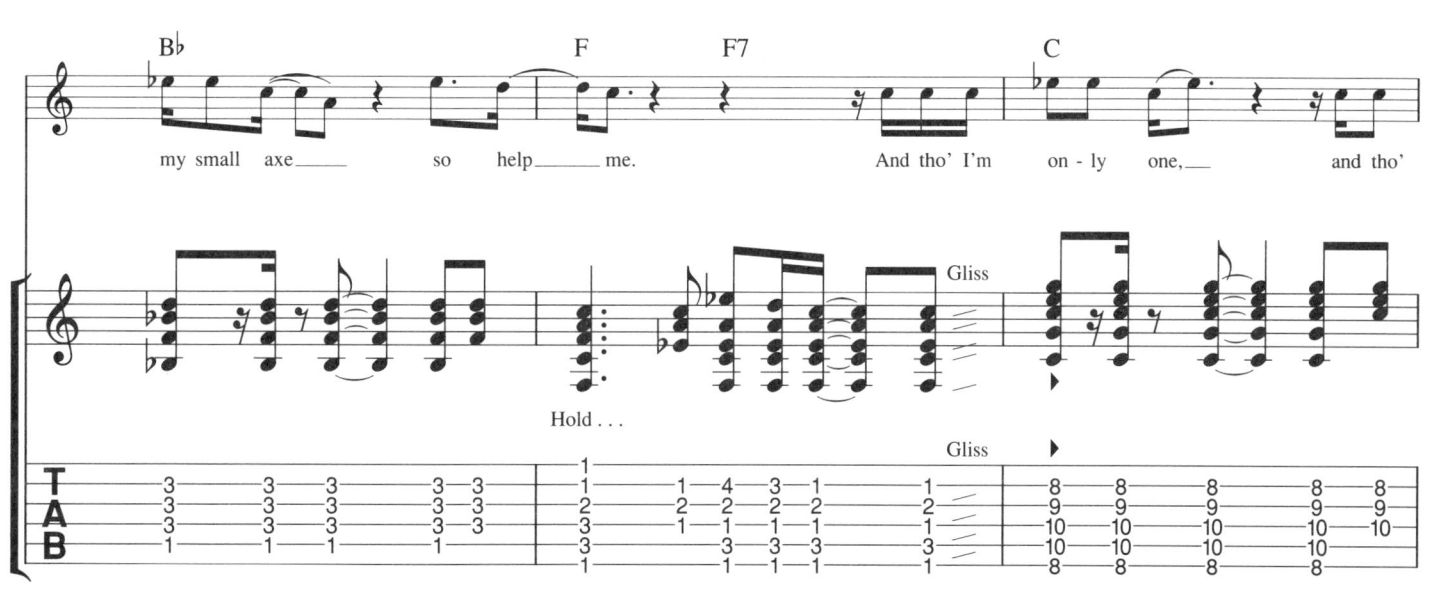

my small axe____ so help____me. And tho' I'm on - ly one,__ and tho'

weak I'm strong___ and if I comes to the crunch___ then___ I'm the wood-cut-ter's son._____

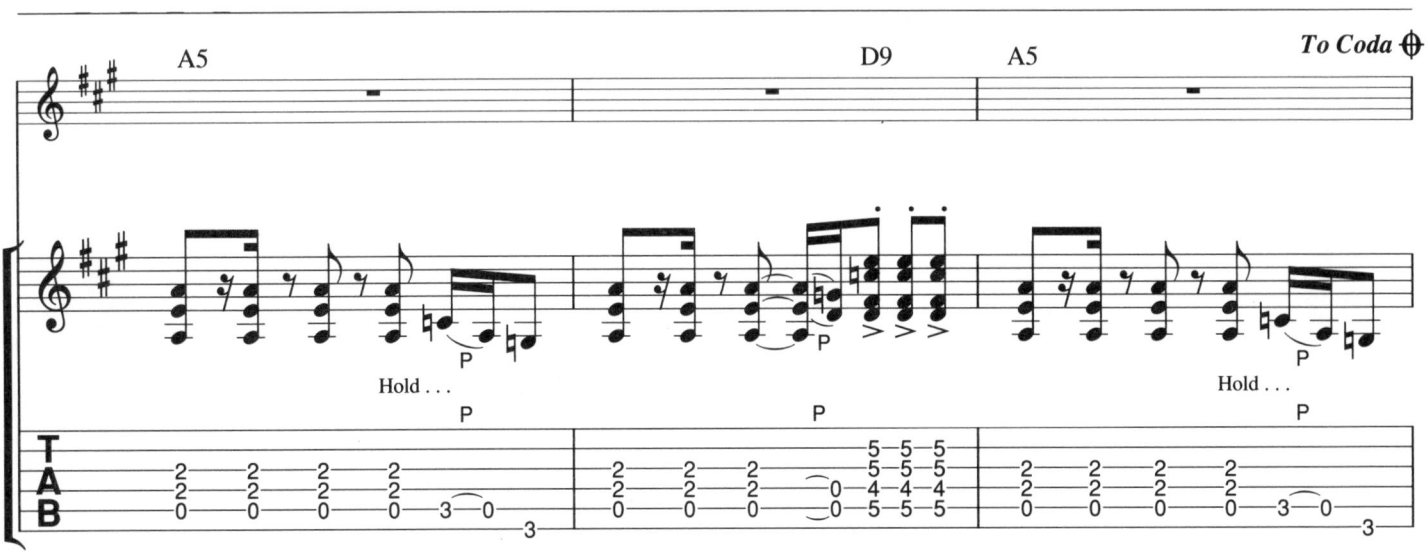

2. You can tell_ wood-cut-ter's son._____

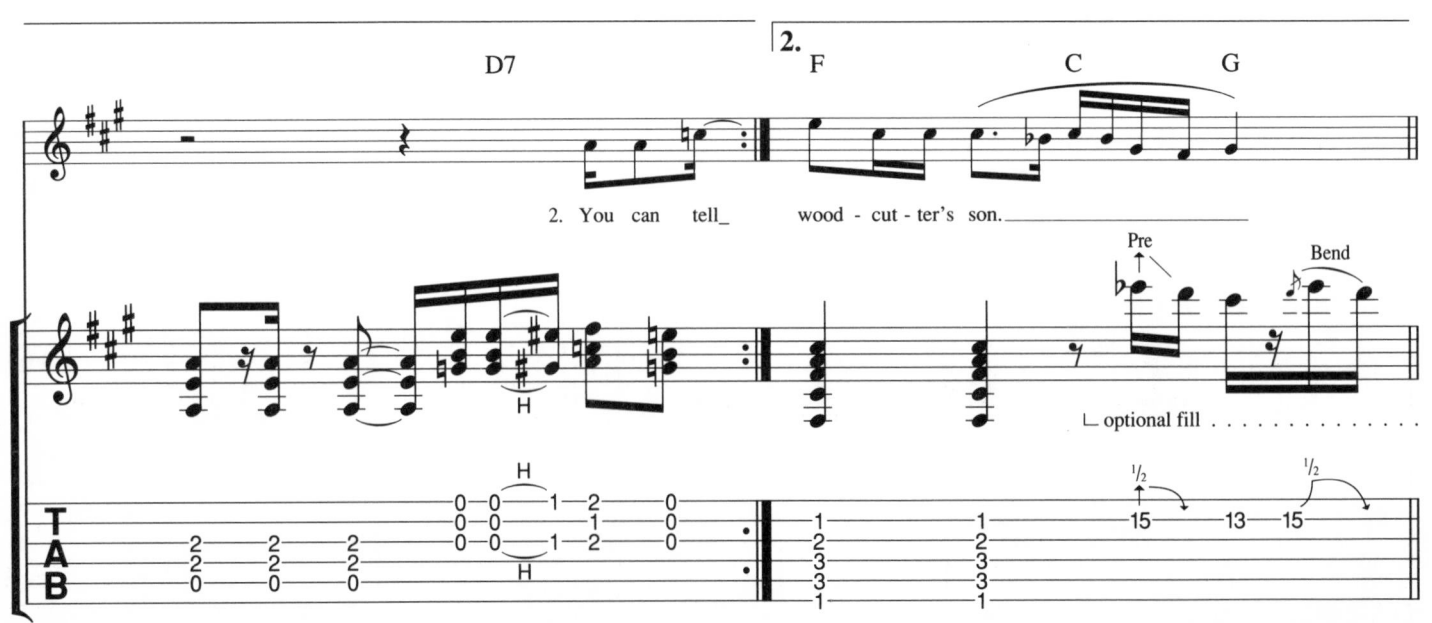

Cut - ting down the wood for the good of ev - ery one,____

(optional fill) . . . . ⌐

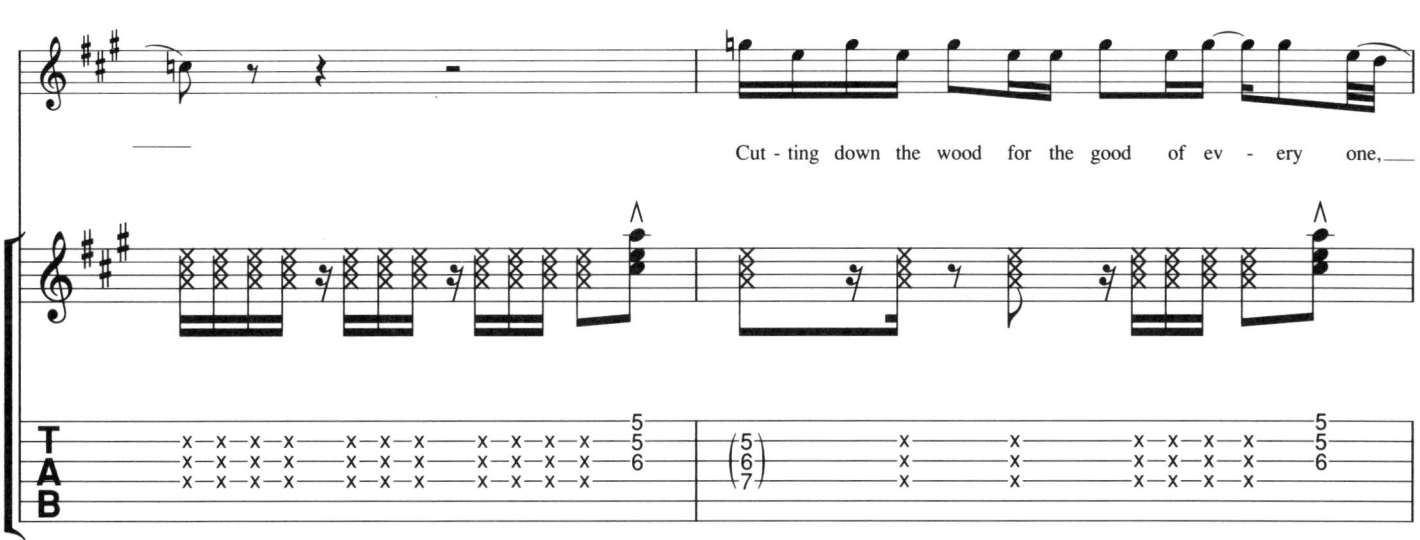

Cut - ting down the wood for the good of ev - ery one,____

Piano solo

A5

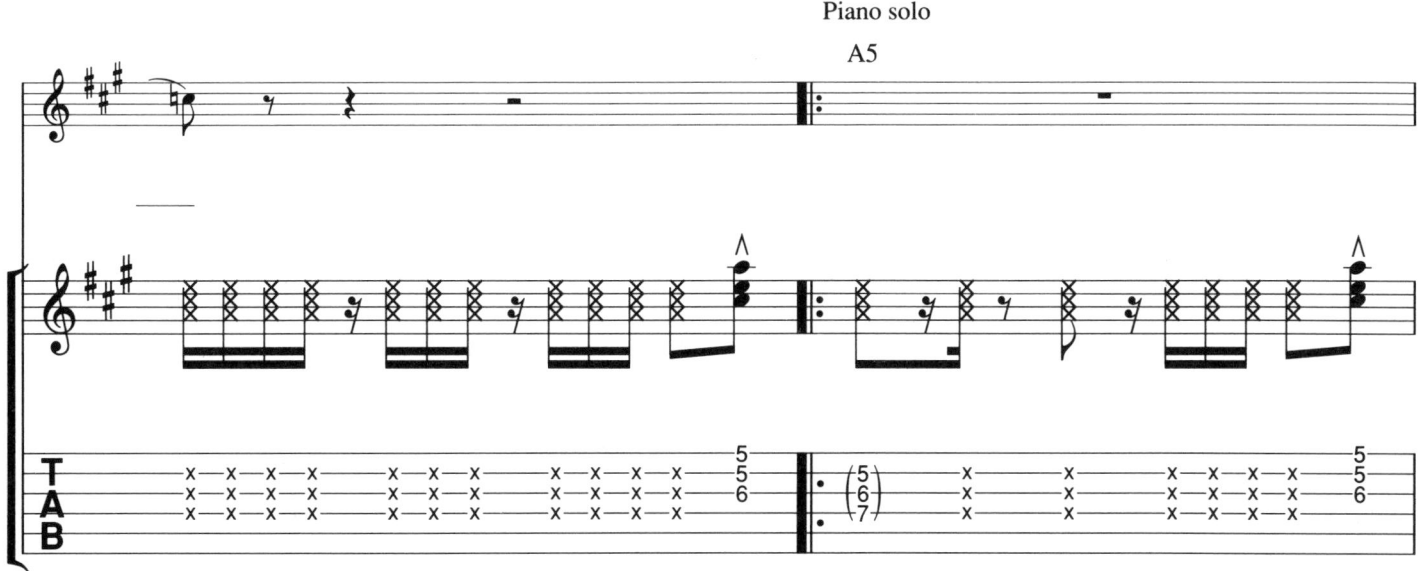

Play 3 times

3. There's a si-(lence)

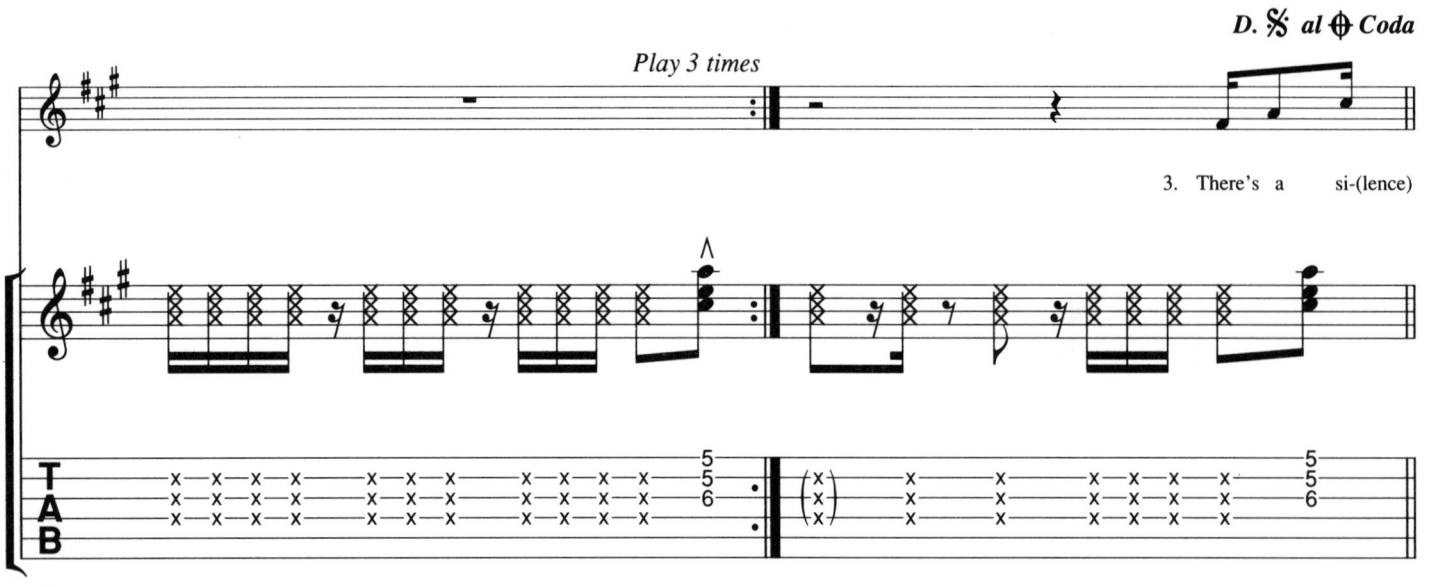

Coda ⊕   A5   D   A5

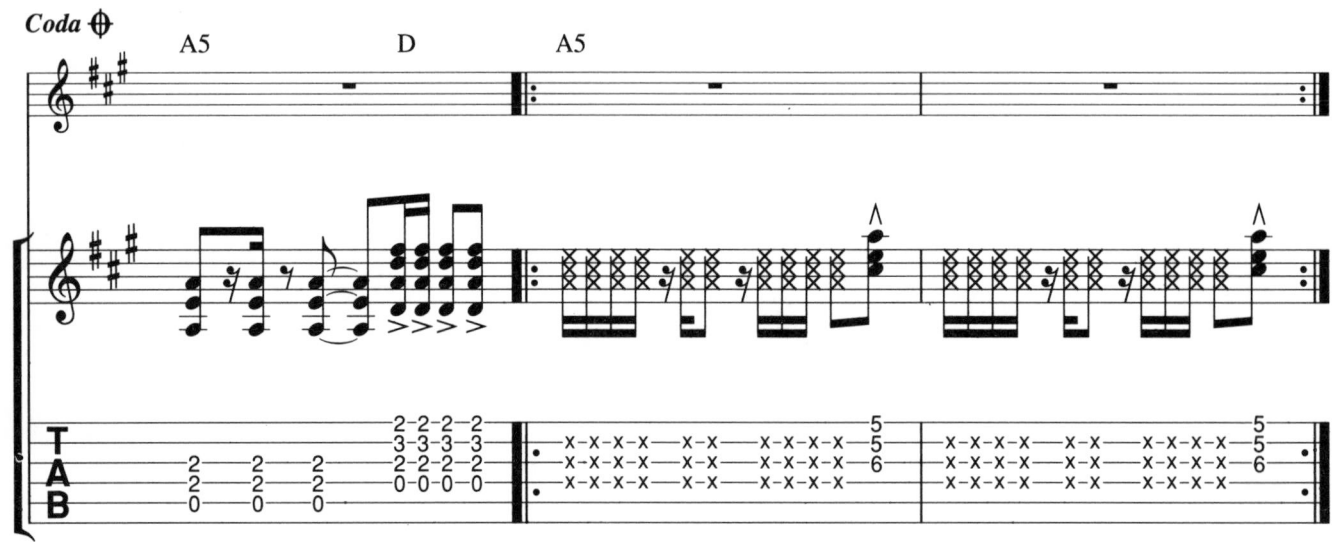

A5

Cut - ting down the wood for the good of ev - ery - one._____   So I'm

cut - ting down the wood   for the good   of ev - ery   one._____   Yeah,   I'm

Verse 2:
You can tell yeah, it's witching hour
You can feel the spirits rise
When the room goes very quiet
And there's hatred in their eyes.

Verse 4(𝄋)
There's a silence when I enter
And a murmur when I leave
And I can see their jealous faces
Oh, I can feel the ice they breathe.

the changingman

words by paul weller
music by paul weller & brendan lynch

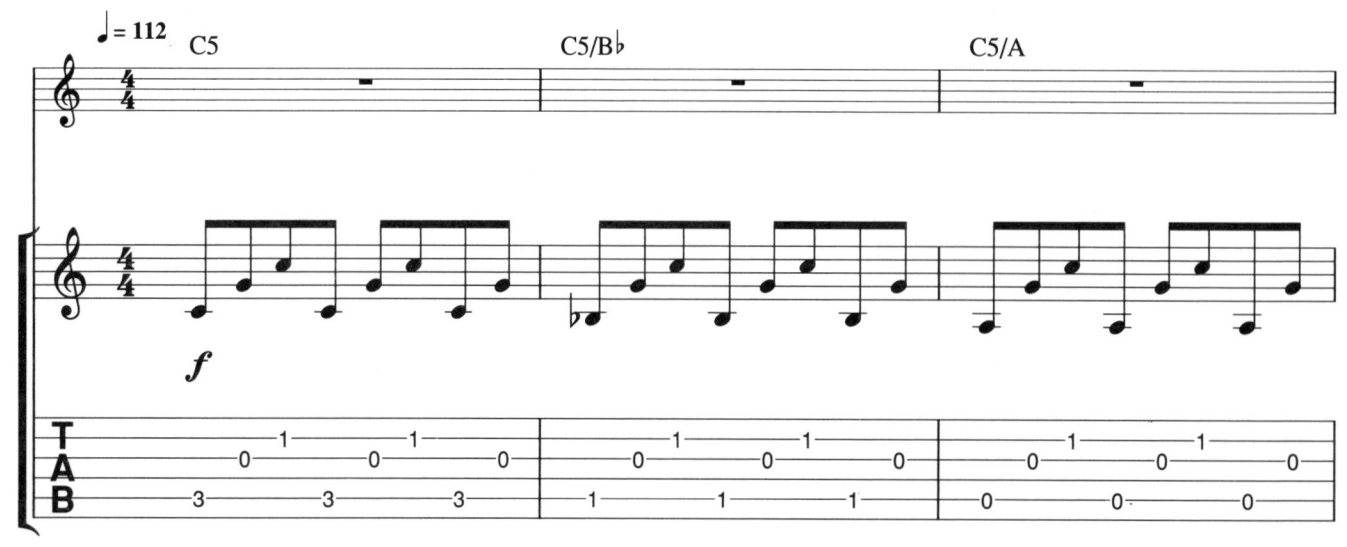

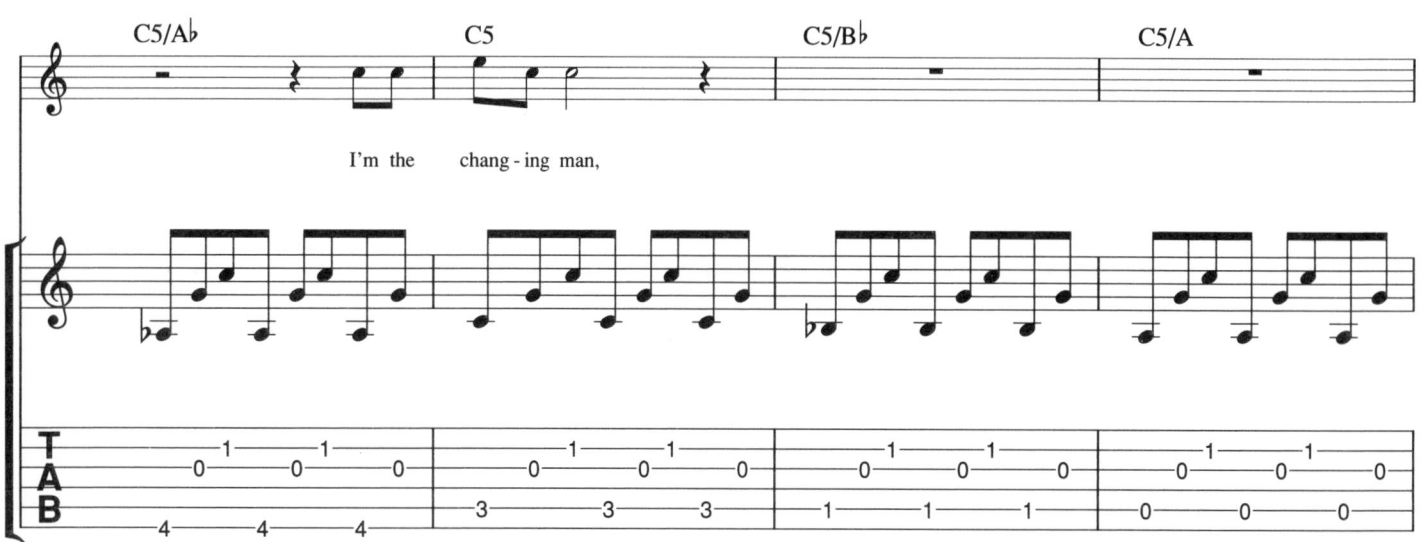

I'm the chang-ing man,

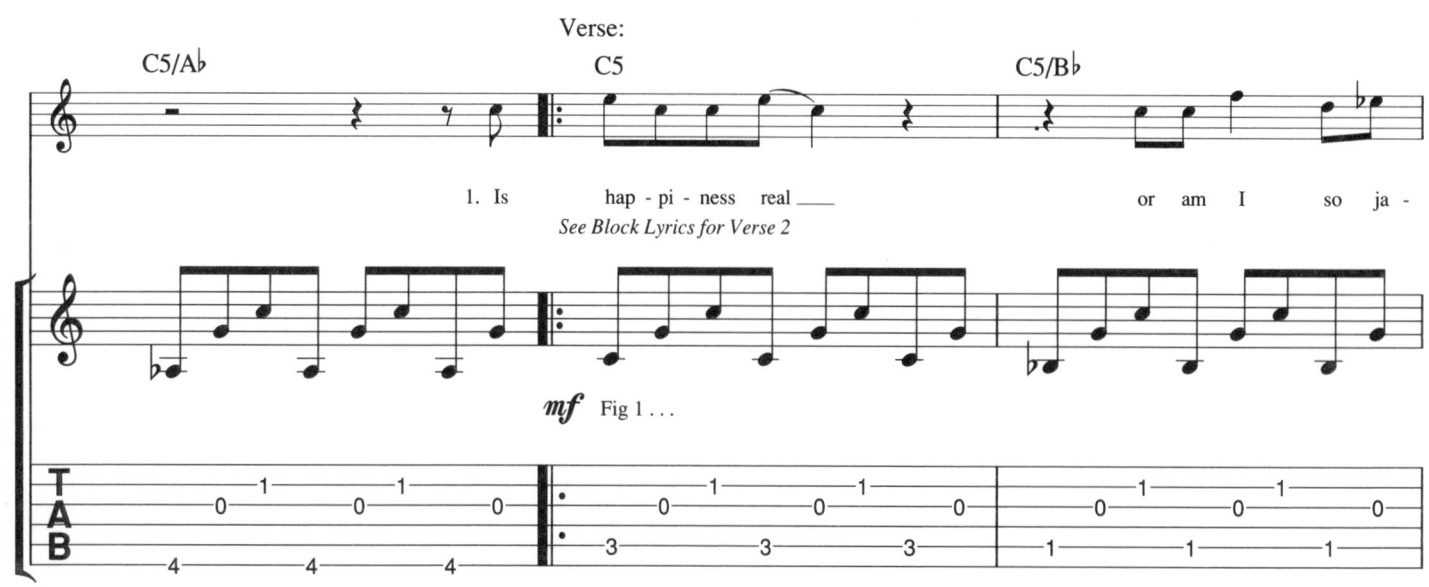

Verse:

1. Is hap-pi-ness real ___ or am I so ja-
See Block Lyrics for Verse 2

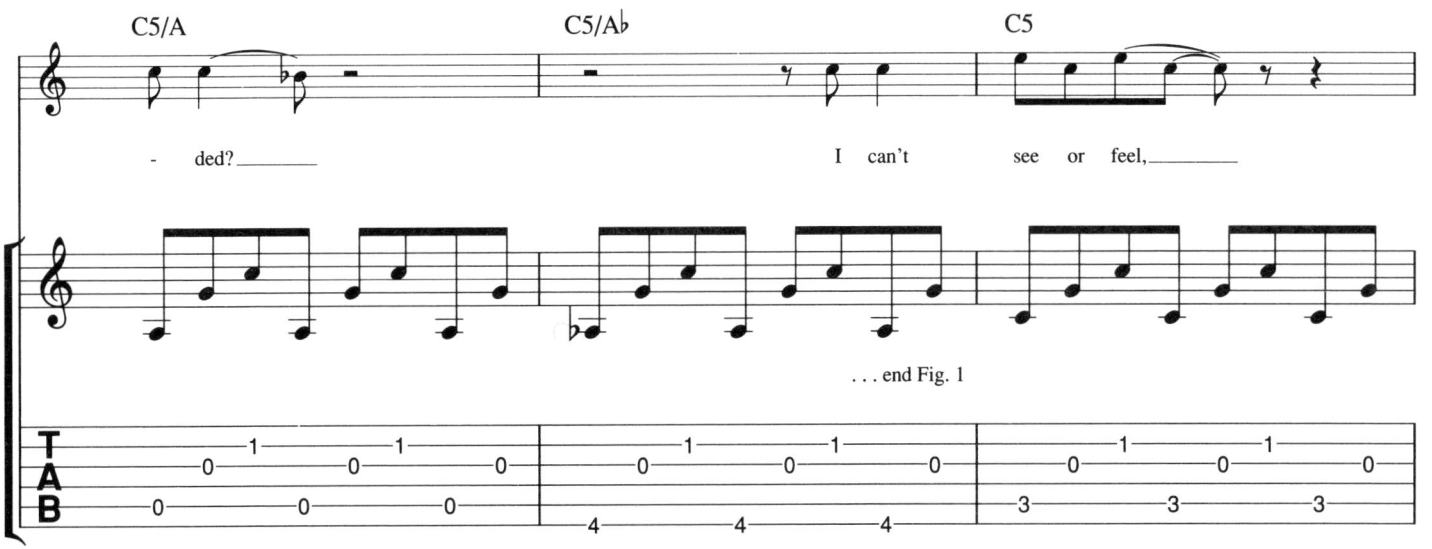

- ded?_____   I can't   see or feel,_____

. . . end Fig. 1

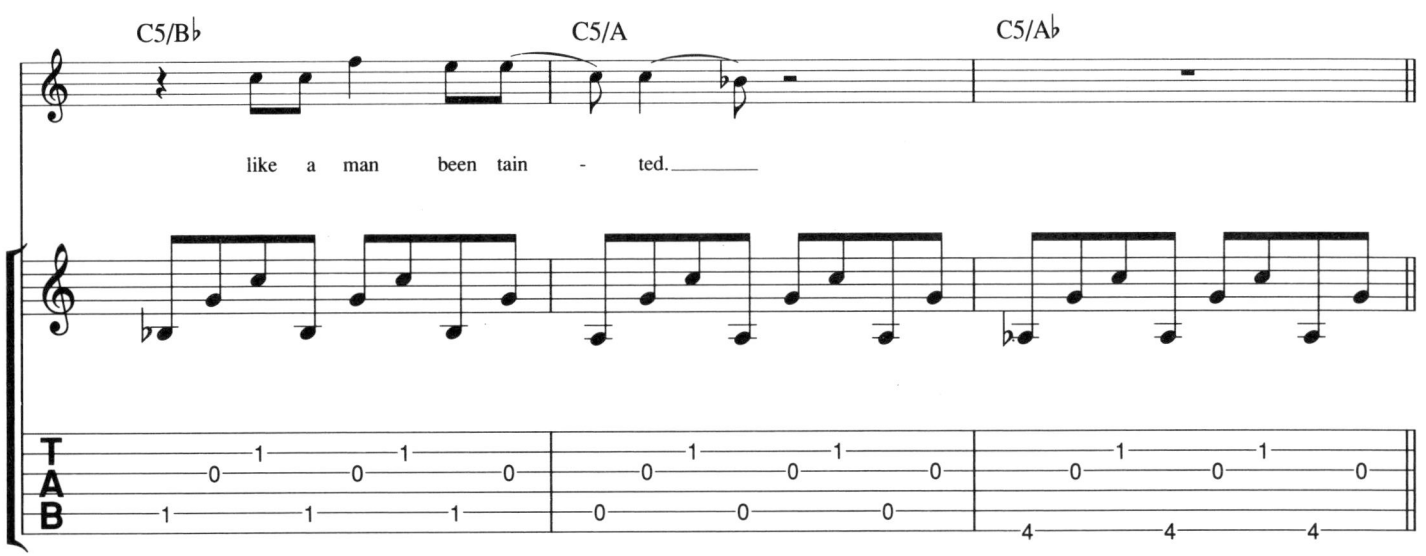

like a man   been tain - ted._____

Numbed by the ef-fect._____   a - ware of the muse,___   too in   touch with my-self,___   I

light the fuse,___ I'm the chang-ing man,_____ oh,___ I'm built on

shift - ing sand._____ Yeah,_____ I'm the chang - ing man,

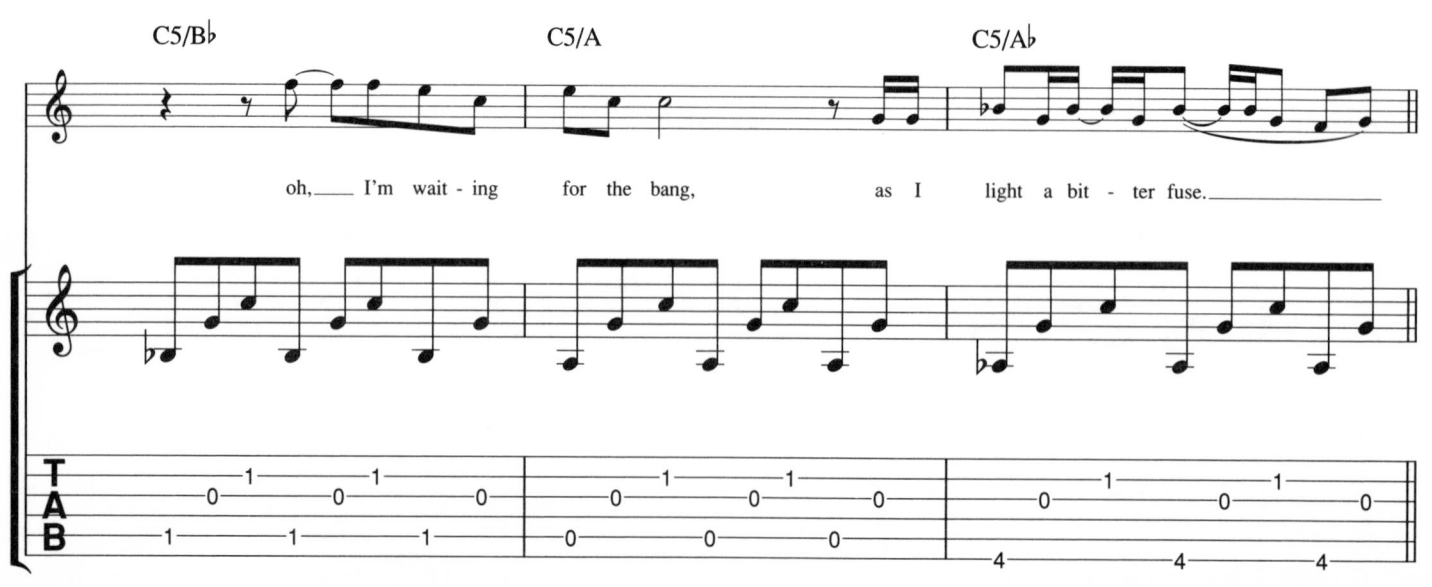

oh,___ I'm wait - ing for the bang, as I light a bit - ter fuse._____

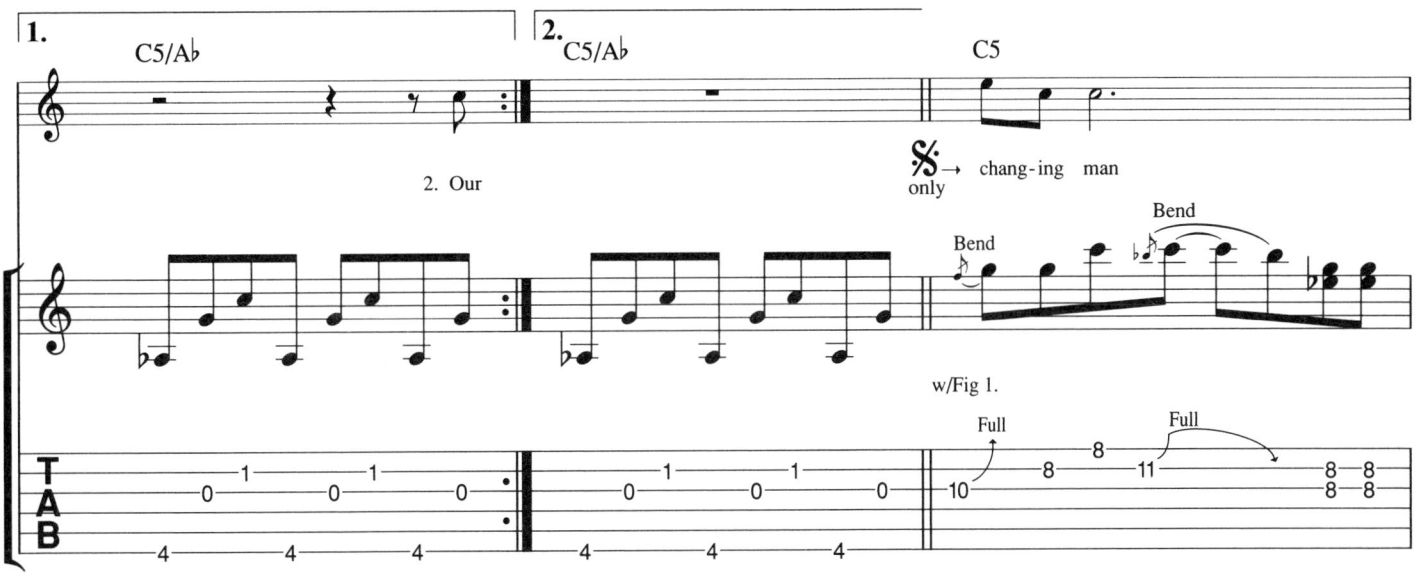

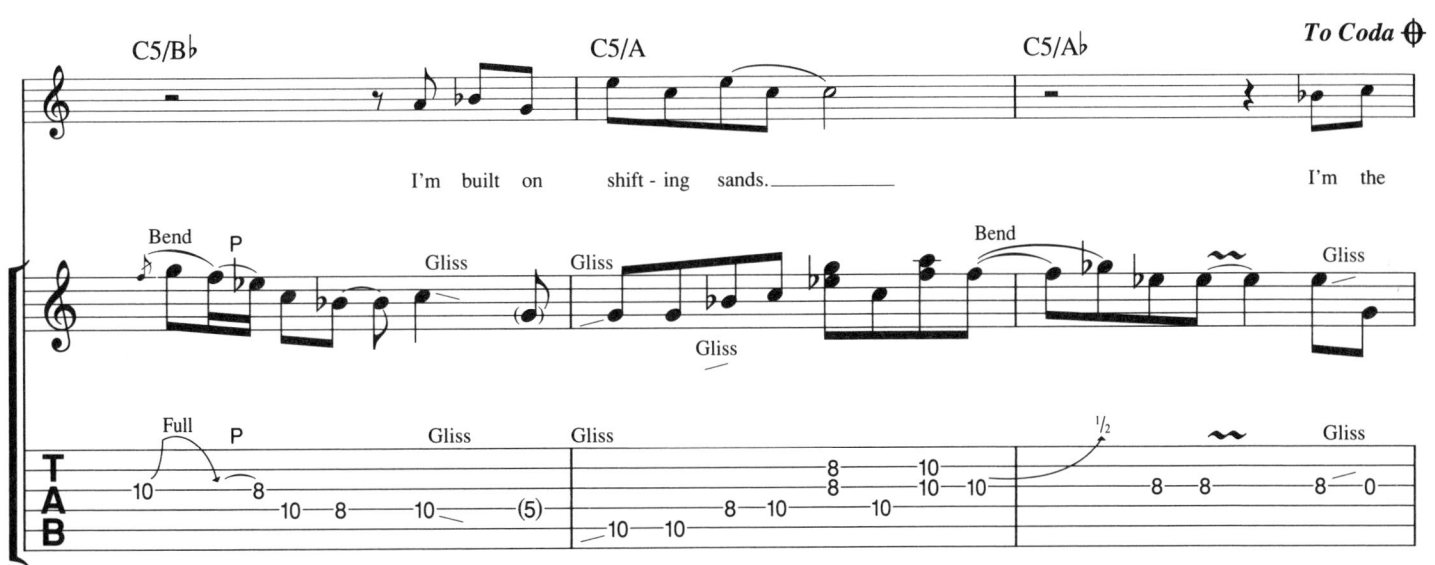

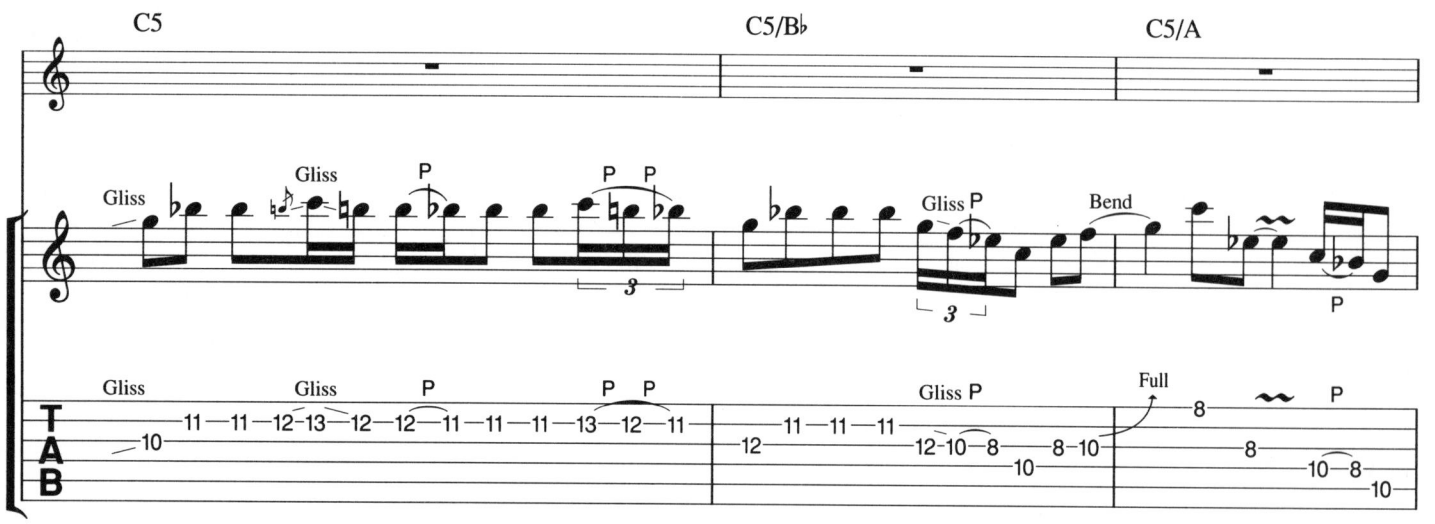

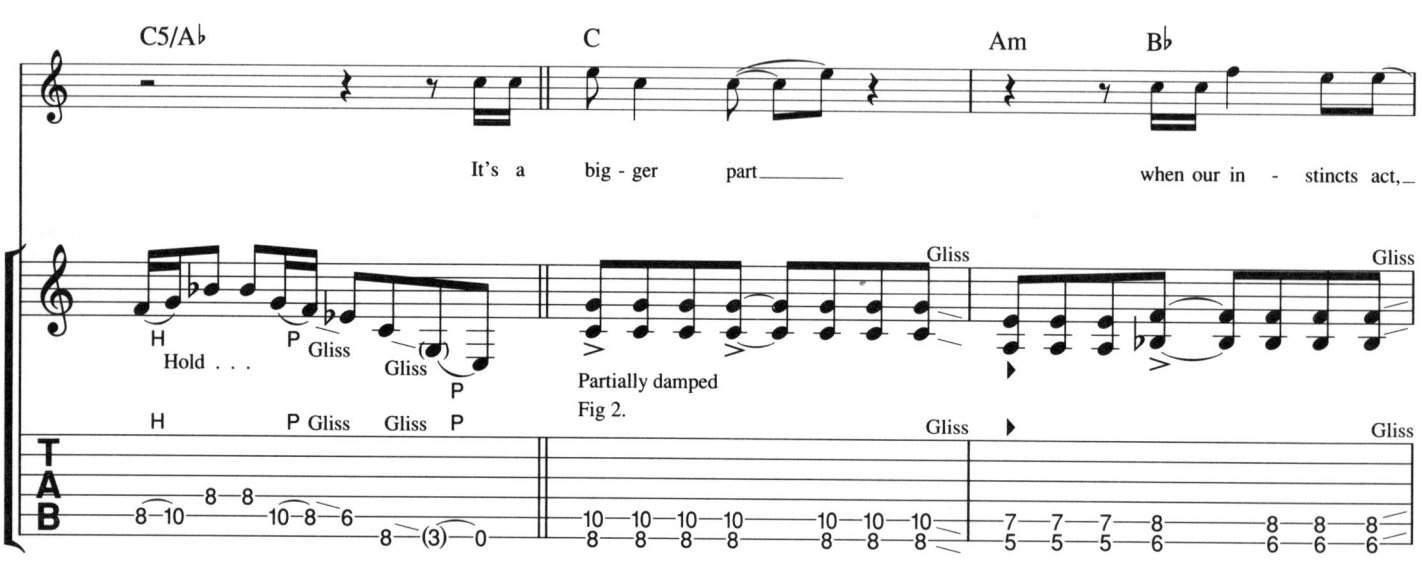

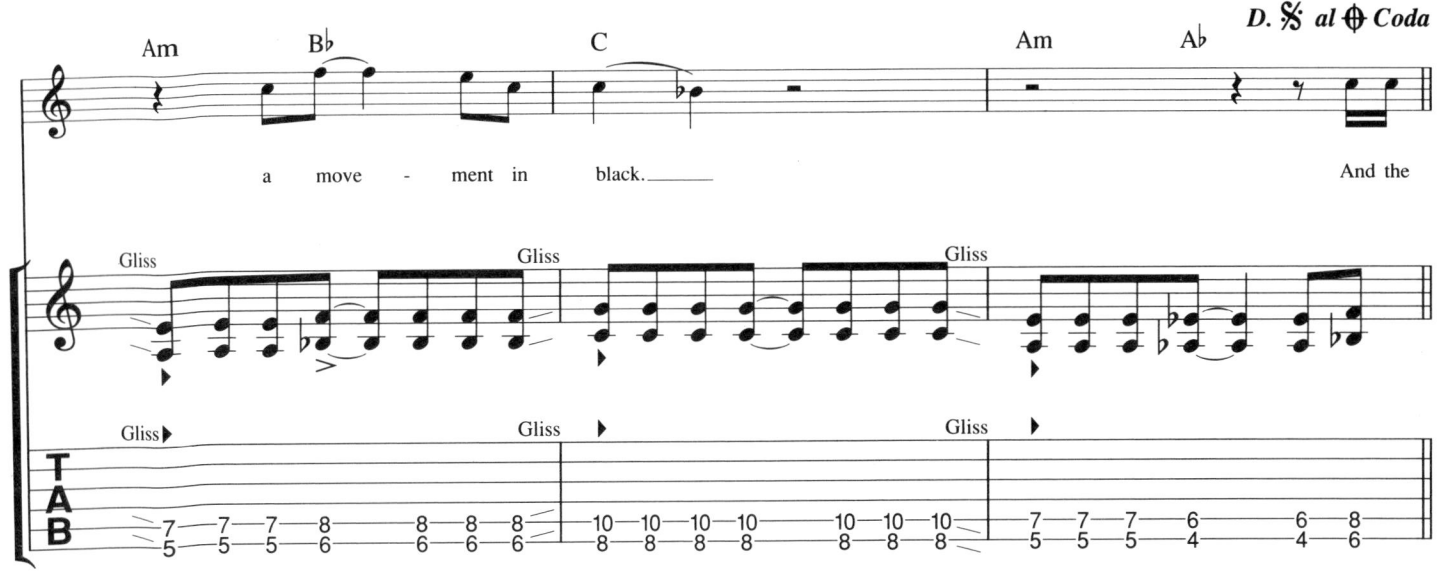

Verse 2:
Our time is on loan
Only ours to borrow
What I can't be today
I can be tomorrow.

Bridge 2 and 𝄋:
And the more I see
The more I know
The more I know
The less I understand.